MUSE
Hullabaloo
SOUNDTRACK

GUITAR

TAB

EDITION

GW00536161

Sony Music Publishing (Japan) Inc.

Exclusive distributors:
Music Sales Limited
8/9 Frith Street, London W1D 3JB, England.
Music Sales Pty Limited
120 Rothschild Avenue, Rosebery, NSW 2018, Australia.

Order No. AM975326
ISBN 0-7119-9649-0
This book © Copyright 2002 by Taste Media Limited.

Music arrangements by
Keith Hawkins, Pete Whittard & Martin Shellard.
Music processed by The Pitts.

Printed in the United Kingdom by
Printwise (Haverhill) Limited, Suffolk.

www.musicsales.com

Your Guarantee of Quality:

As publishers, we strive to produce every book
to the highest commercial standards.

While endeavouring to retain the original running
order of the recorded album, the book has been
carefully designed to minimise awkward page turns
and to make playing from it a real pleasure.

Particular care has been given to specifying
acid-free, neutral-sized paper made from pulps which
have not been elemental chlorine bleached.

This pulp is from farmed sustainable forests and
was produced with special regard for the environment.

Throughout, the printing and binding have been
planned to ensure a sturdy, attractive publication
which should give years of enjoyment.

If your copy fails to meet our high standards,
please inform us and we will gladly replace it.

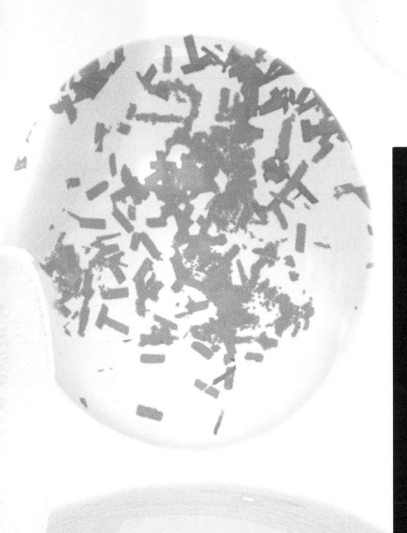

FORCED IN 8

SHRINKING UNIVERSE 11

RECESS 16

YES PLEASE 23

MAP OF YOUR HEAD 28

NATURE_1 33

SHINE ACOUSTIC 42

ASHAMED 48

THE GALLERY 55

HYPER CHONDRIAC MUSIC 60

DEAD STAR 66

MICRO CUTS 73

CITIZEN ERASED 80

SHOWBIZ 96

MEGALOMANIA 107

DARK SHINES 114

SCREENAGER 123

SPACE DEMENTIA 128

IN YOUR WORLD 137

MUSCLE MUSEUM 150

AGITATED 144

GUITAR TABLATURE EXPLAINED 6

GUITAR TABLATURE EXPLAINED

Guitar music can be notated three different ways: on a musical stave, in tablature, and in rhythm slashes.

RHYTHM SLASHES are written above the stave. Strum chords in the rhythm indicated. Round noteheads indicate single notes.

THE MUSICAL STAVE shows pitches and rhythms and is divided by lines into bars. Pitches are named after the first seven letters of the alphabet.

TABLATURE graphically represents the guitar fingerboard. Each horizontal line represents a string, and each number represents a fret.

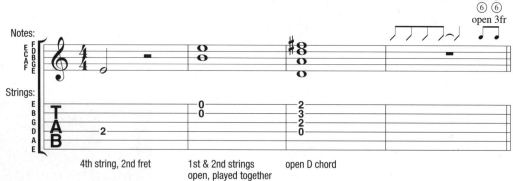

4th string, 2nd fret

1st & 2nd strings open, played together

open D chord

DEFINITIONS FOR SPECIAL GUITAR NOTATION

SEMI-TONE BEND: Strike the note and bend up a semi-tone (1/2 step).

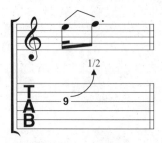

WHOLE-TONE BEND: Strike the note and bend up a whole-tone (whole step).

GRACE NOTE BEND: Strike the note and bend as indicated. Play the first note as quickly as possible.

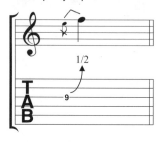

QUARTER-TONE BEND: Strike the note and bend up a 1/4 step.

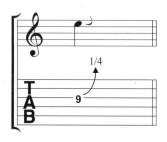

BEND & RELEASE: Strike the note and bend up as indicated, then release back to the original note.

COMPOUND BEND & RELEASE: Strike the note and bend up and down in the rhythm indicated.

PRE-BEND: Bend the note as indicated, then strike it.

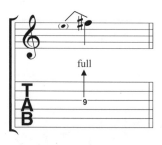

PRE-BEND & RELEASE: Bend the note as indicated. Strike it and release the note back to the original pitch.

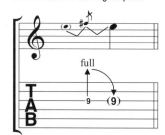

UNISON BEND: Strike the two notes simultaneously and bend the lower note up to the pitch of the higher.

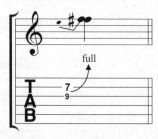

BEND & RESTRIKE: Strike the note and bend as indicated then restrike the string where the symbol occurs.

BEND, HOLD AND RELEASE: Same as bend and release but hold the bend for the duration of the tie.

BEND AND TAP: Bend the note as indicated and tap the higher fret while still holding the bend.

VIBRATO: The string is vibrated by rapidly bending and releasing the note with the fretting hand.

HAMMER-ON: Strike the first note with one finger, then sound the second note (on the same string) with another finger by fretting it without picking.

PULL-OFF: Place both fingers on the notes to be sounded, strike the first note and without picking, pull the finger off to sound the second note.

LEGATO SLIDE (GLISS): Strike the first note and then slide the same fret-hand finger up or down to the second note. The second note is not struck.

NOTE: The speed of any bend is indicated by the music notation and tempo.

SHIFT SLIDE (GLISS & RESTRIKE): Same as legato slide, except the second note is struck.

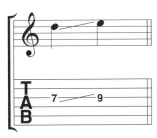

TRILL: Very rapidly alternate between the notes indicated by continuously hammering on and pulling off.

TAPPING: Hammer ("tap") the fret indicated with the pick-hand index or middle finger and pull off to the note fretted by the fret hand.

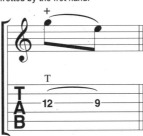

PICK SCRAPE: The edge of the pick is rubbed down (or up) the string, producing a scratchy sound.

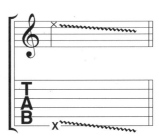

MUFFLED STRINGS: A percussive sound is produced by laying the fret hand across the string(s) without depressing, and striking them with the pick hand.

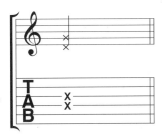

NATURAL HARMONIC: Strike the note while the fret-hand lightly touches the string directly over the fret indicated.

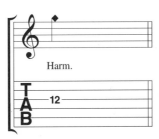

PINCH HARMONIC: The note is fretted normally and a harmonic is produced by adding the edge of the thumb or the tip of the index finger of the pick hand to the normal pick attack.

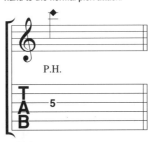

HARP HARMONIC: The note is fretted normally and a harmonic is produced by gently resting the pick hand's index finger directly above the indicated fret (in brackets) while plucking the appropriate string.

PALM MUTING: The note is partially muted by the pick hand lightly touching the string(s) just before the bridge.

RAKE: Drag the pick across the strings indicated with a single motion.

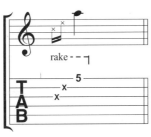

TREMOLO PICKING: The note is picked as rapidly and continuously as possible.

ARPEGGIATE: Play the notes of the chord indicated by quickly rolling them from bottom to top.

SWEEP PICKING: Rhythmic downstroke and/or upstroke motion across the strings.

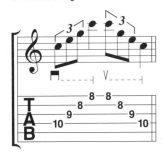

VIBRATO DIVE BAR AND RETURN: The pitch of the note or chord is dropped a specific number of steps (in rhythm) then returned to the original pitch.

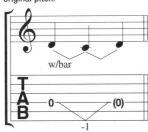

VIBRATO BAR SCOOP: Depress the bar just before striking the note, then quickly release the bar.

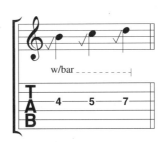

VIBRATO BAR DIP: Strike the note and then immediately drop a specific number of steps, then release back to the original pitch.

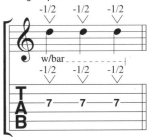

ADDITIONAL MUSICAL DEFINITIONS

 (accent)
- Accentuate note (play it louder).

 (accent)
- Accentuate note with great intensity.

(staccato)
- Shorten time value of note.

- Downstroke

V
- Upstroke

D.%. al Coda
- Go back to the sign (%), then play until the bar marked *To Coda* ⊕ then skip to the section marked ⊕ *Coda*.

D.C. al Fine
- Go back to the beginning of the song and play until the bar marked *Fine*.

tacet
- Instrument is silent (drops out).

- Repeat bars between signs.

1. **2.**
- When a repeated section has different endings, play the first ending only the first time and the second ending only the second time.

NOTE: Tablature numbers in brackets mean:
1. The note is sustained, but a new articulation (such as hammer on or slide) begins.
2. A note may be fretted but not necessarily played.

FORCED IN

Lyrics & Music by Matthew Bellamy

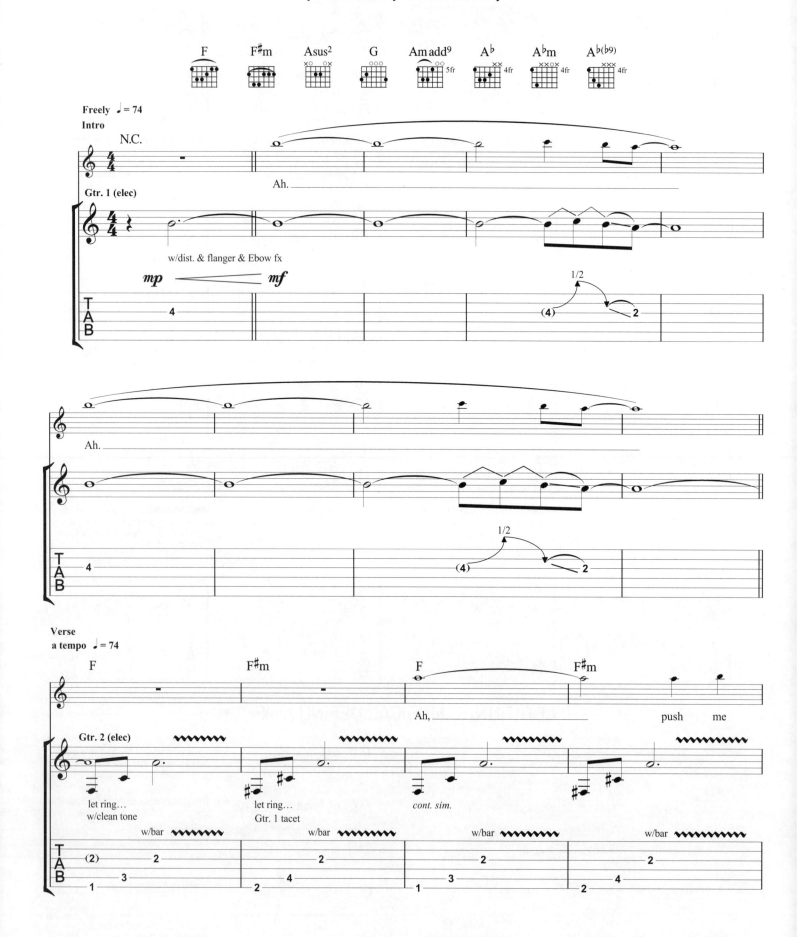

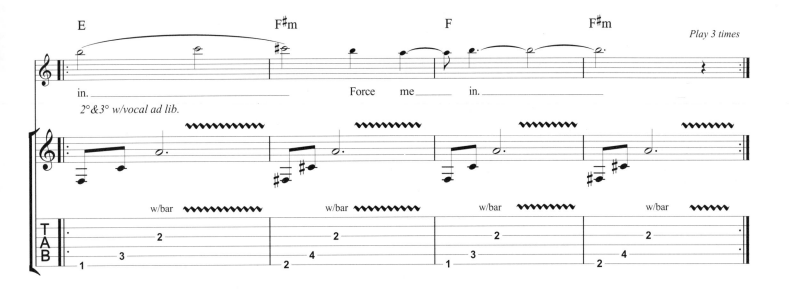

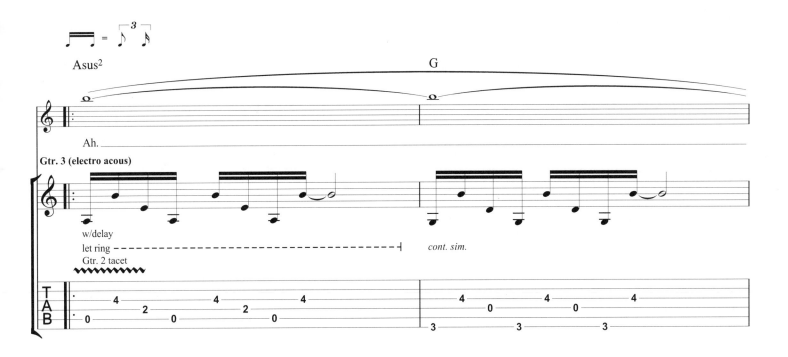

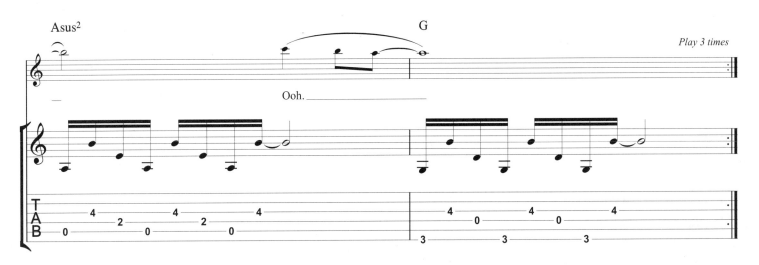

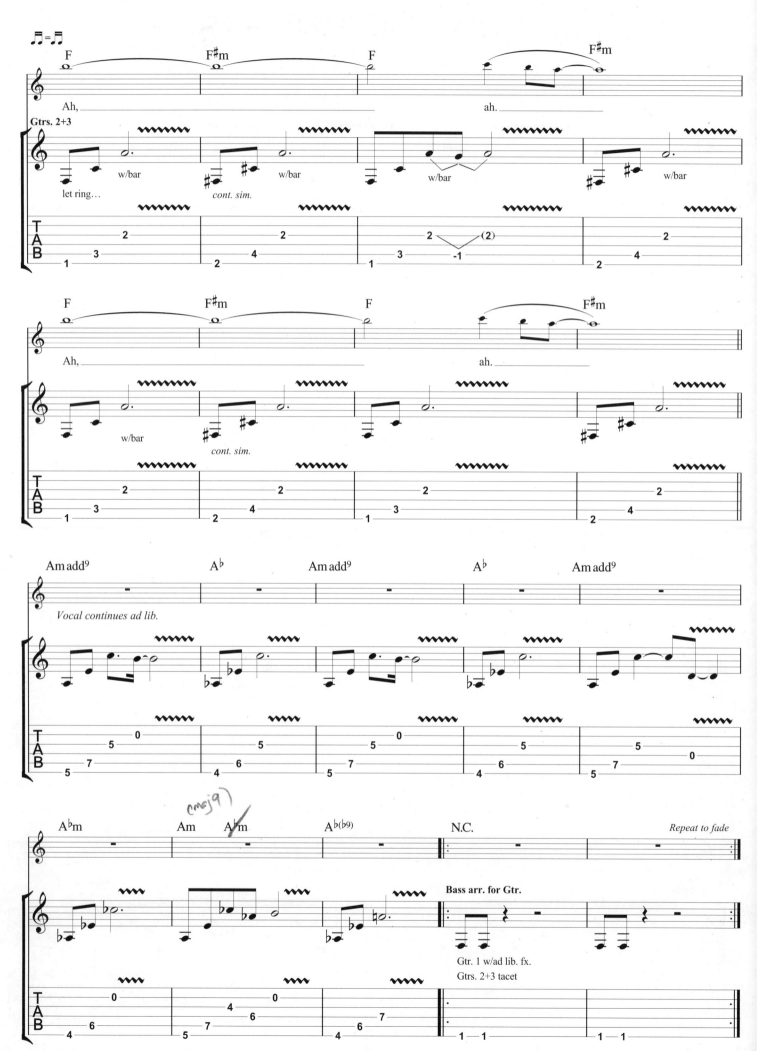

10

SHRINKING UNIVERSE

Lyrics & Music by Matthew Bellamy

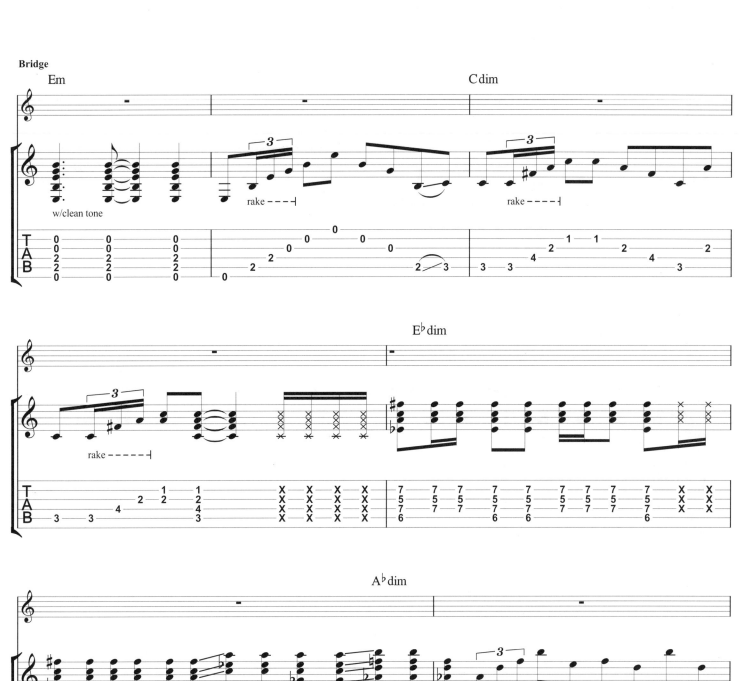

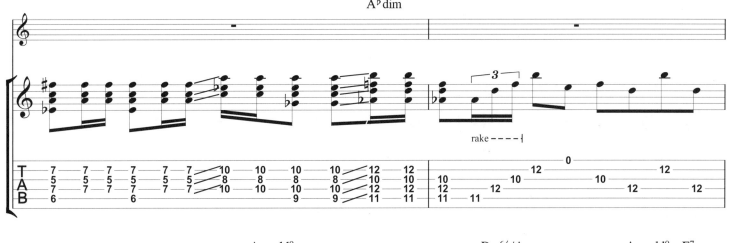

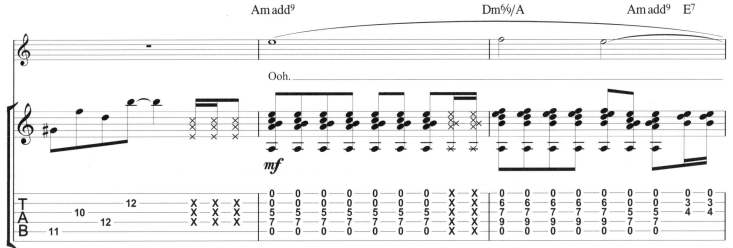

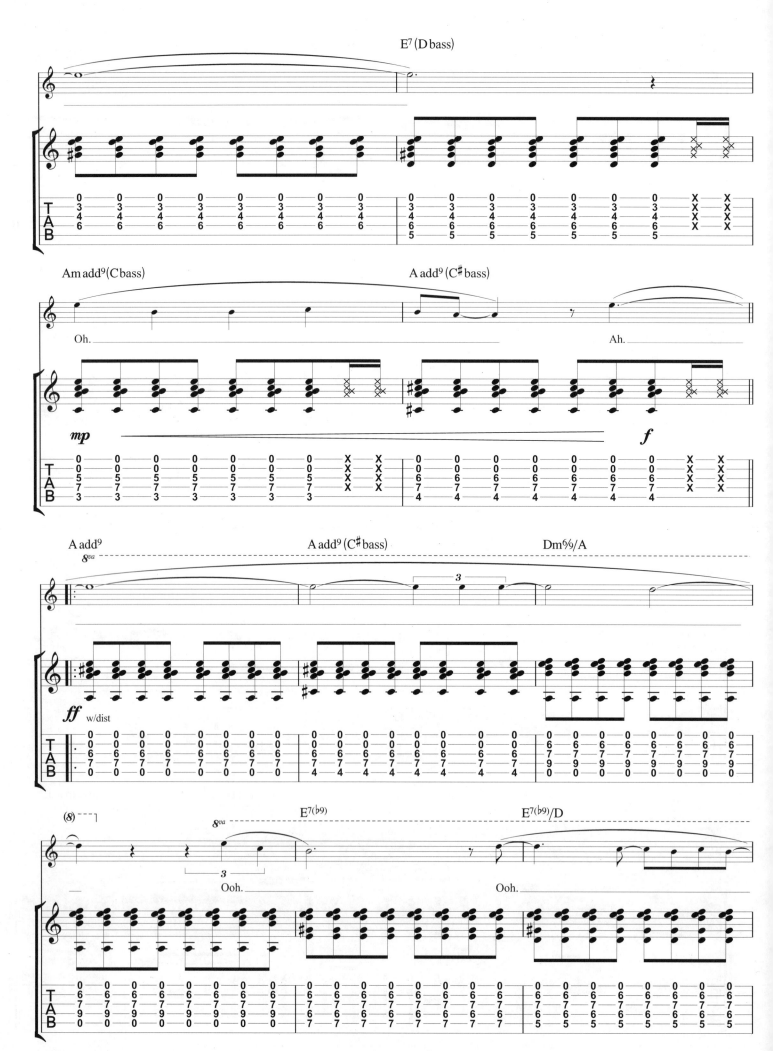

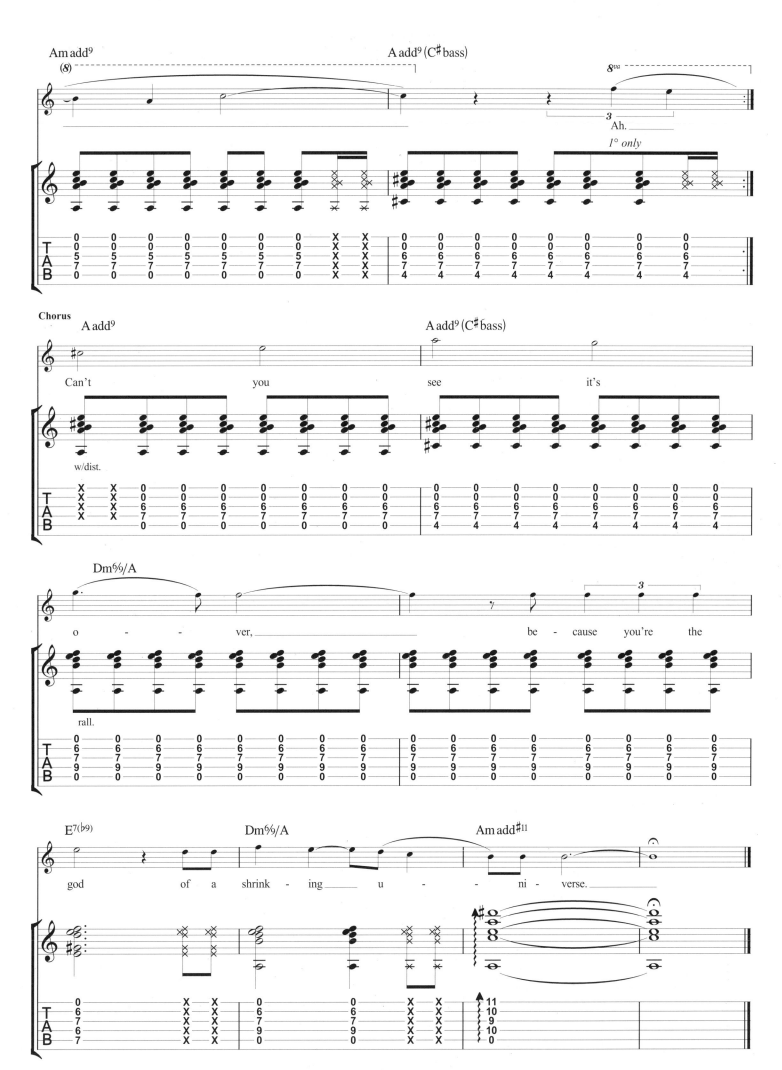

RECESS

Lyrics & Music by Matthew Bellamy

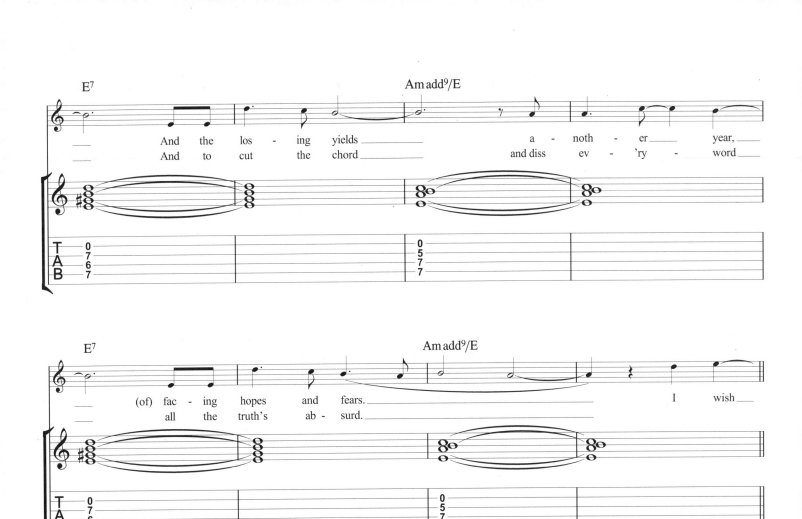

And the los - ing yields _____ a - noth - er _____ year,
And to cut the chord _____ and diss ev - 'ry - word

(of) fac - ing hopes and fears. _____ I wish _____
all the truth's ab - surd. _____

Chorus

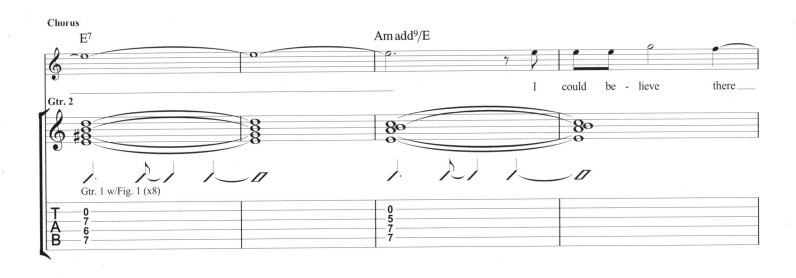

I could be - lieve there _____

Gtr. 2

Gtr. 1 w/Fig. 1 (x8)

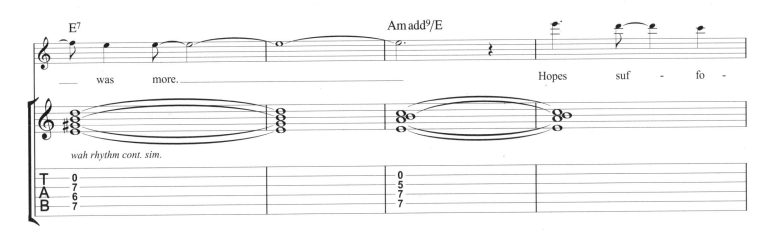

_____ was more. _____ Hopes suf - fo -

wah rhythm cont. sim.

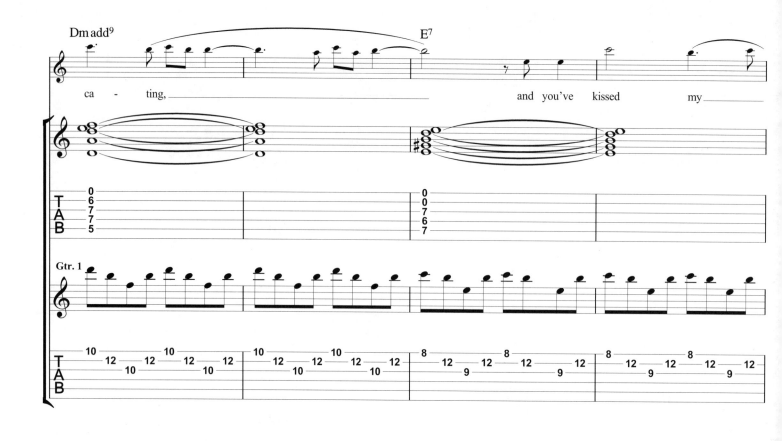

*w/whammy pedal

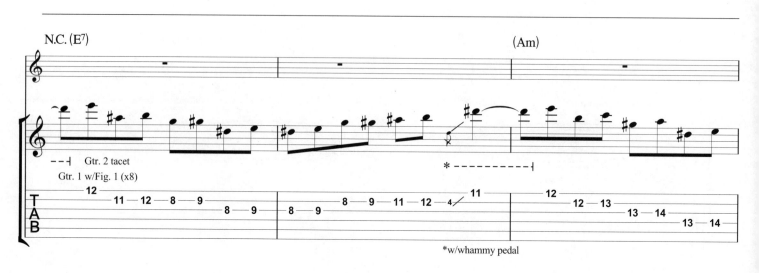

*w/whammy pedal

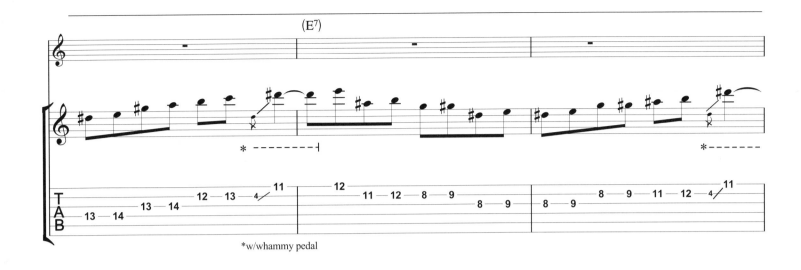

*w/whammy pedal

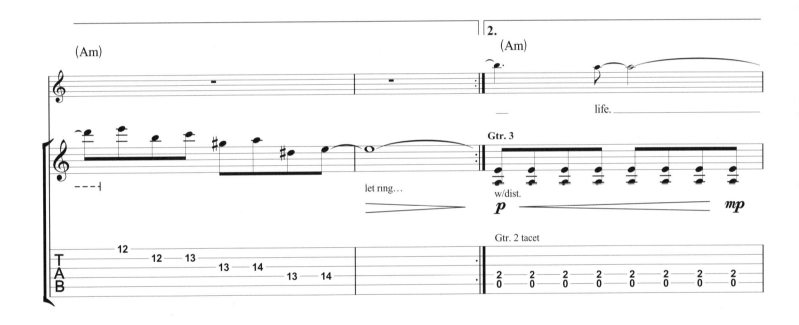

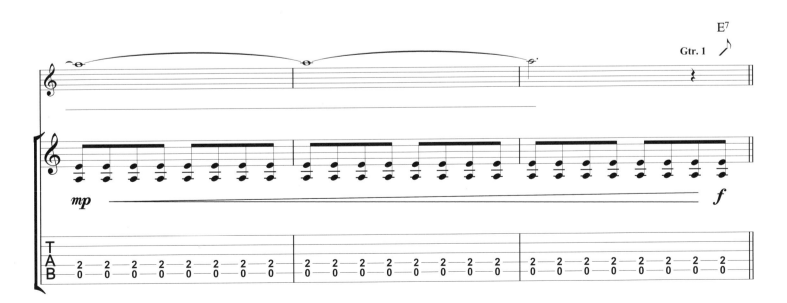

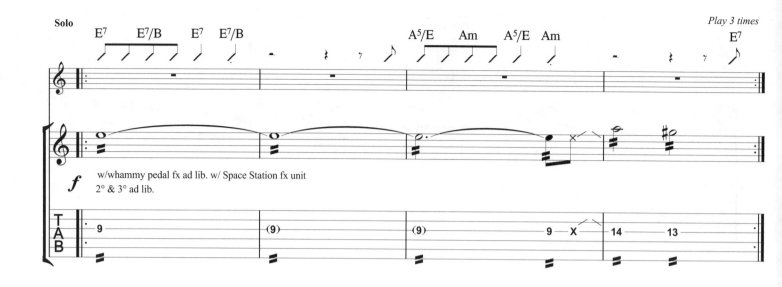

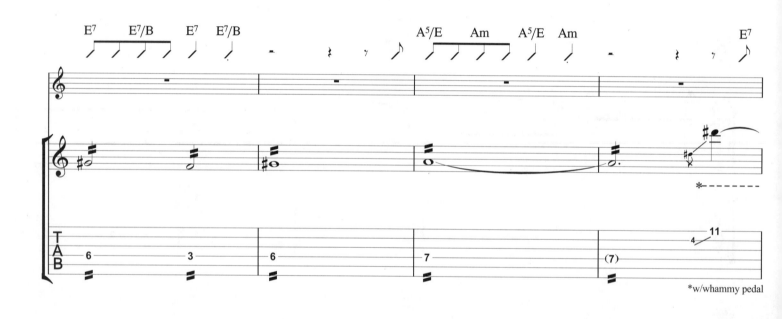

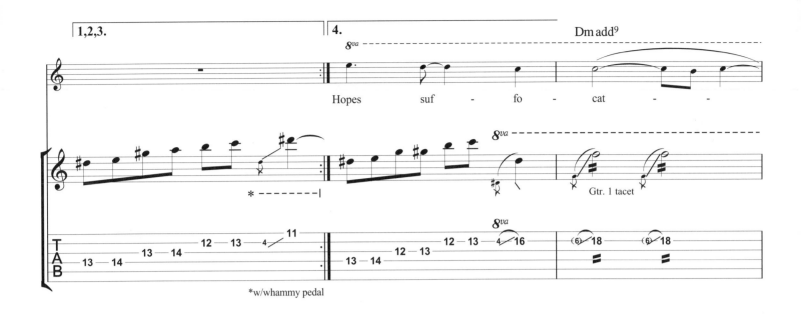

*w/whammy pedal

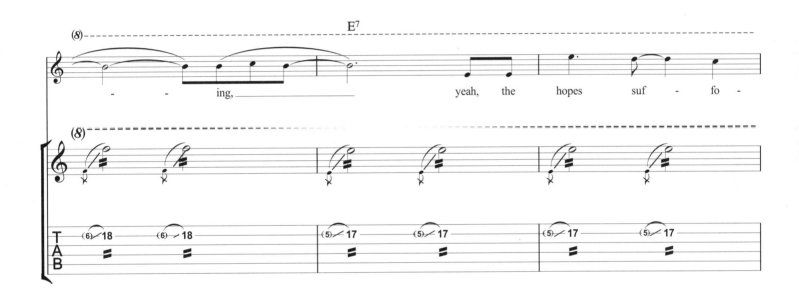

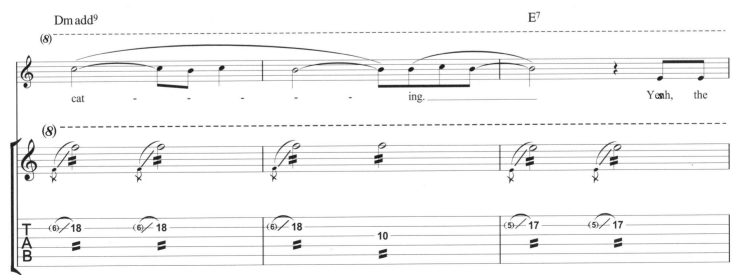

21

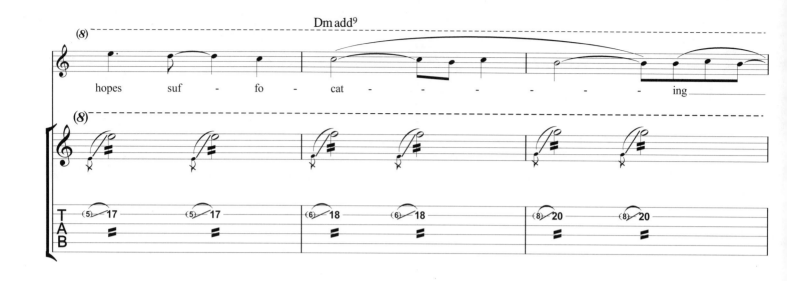

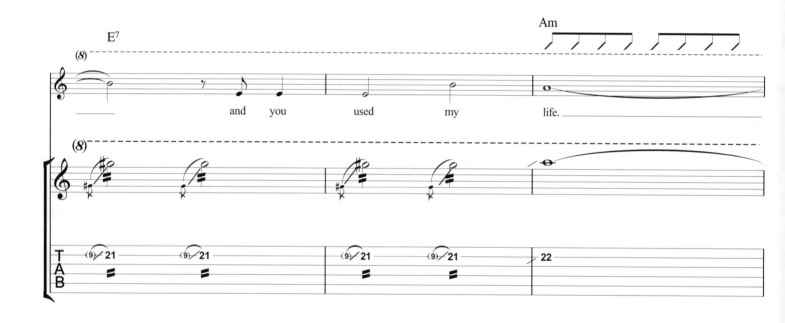

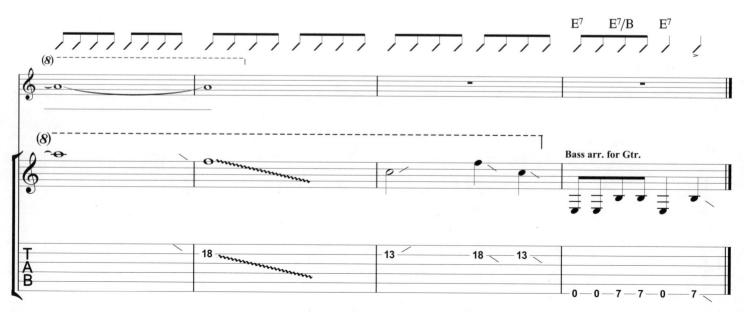

YES PLEASE

Lyrics & Music by Matthew Bellamy

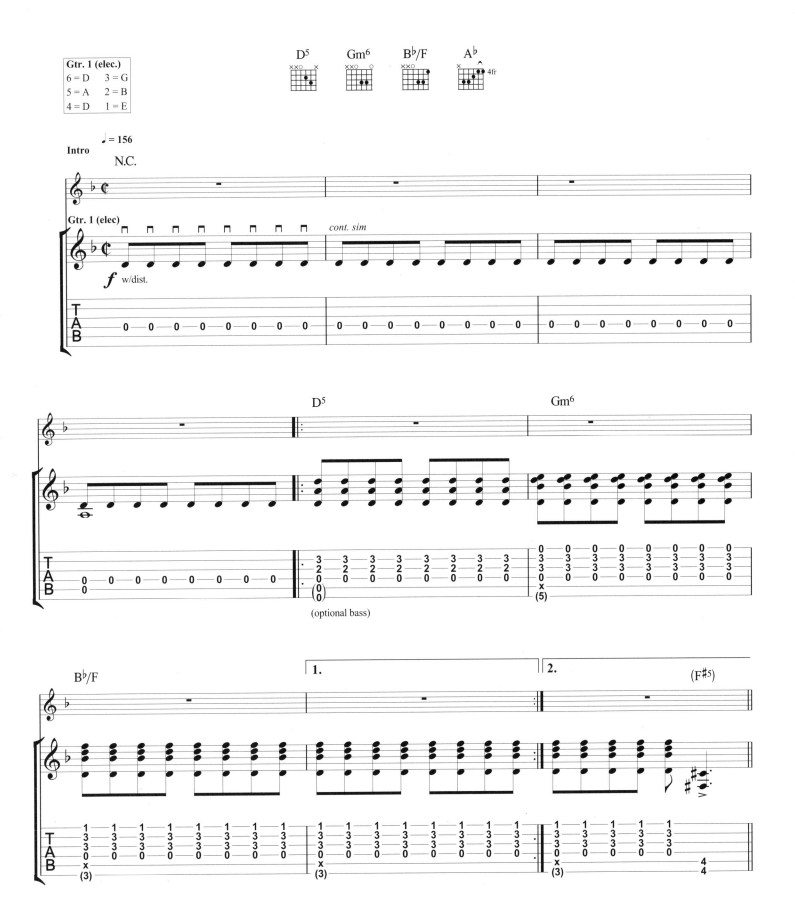

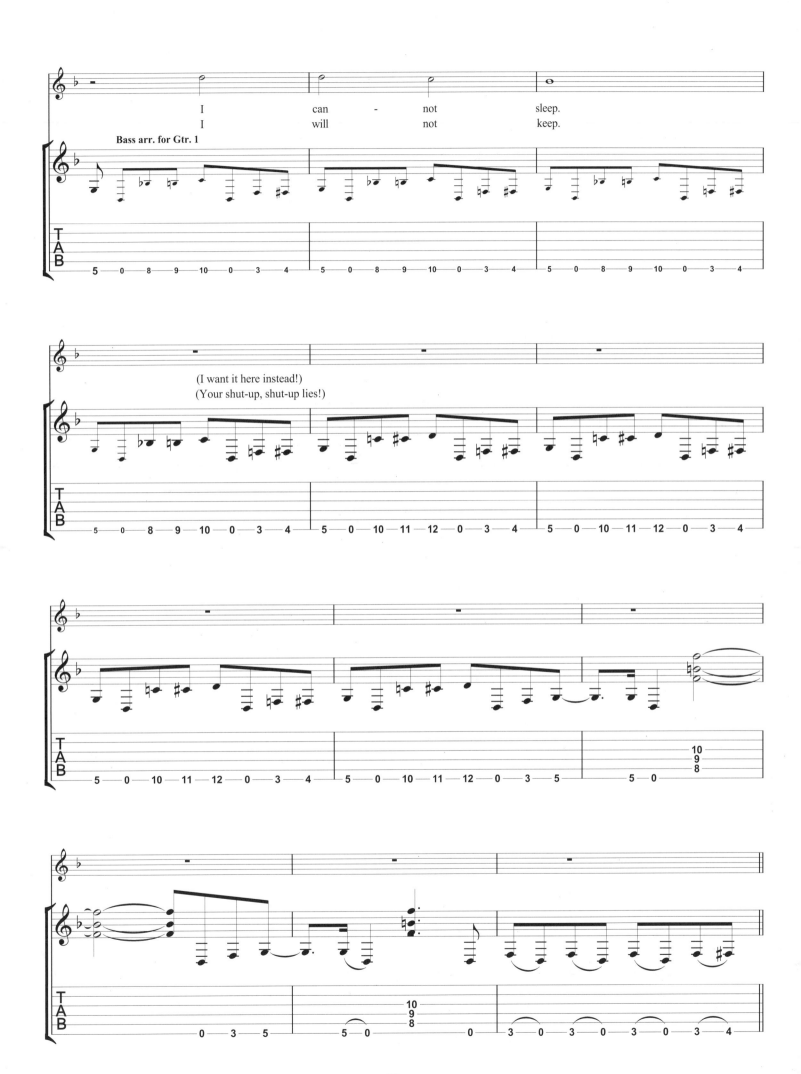

I can - not sleep.
I will not keep.

(I want it here instead!)
(Your shut-up, shut-up lies!)

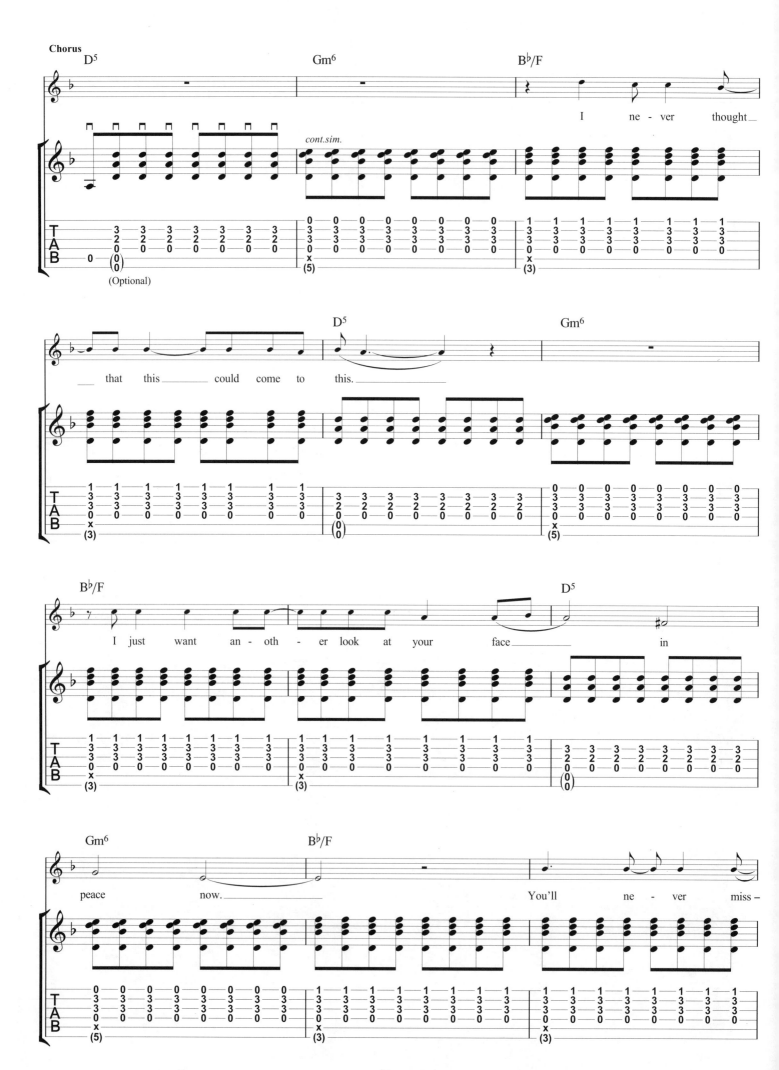

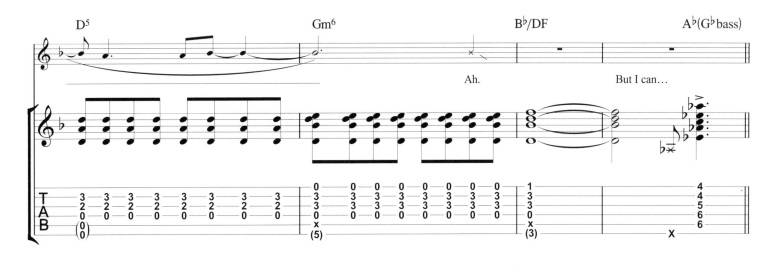

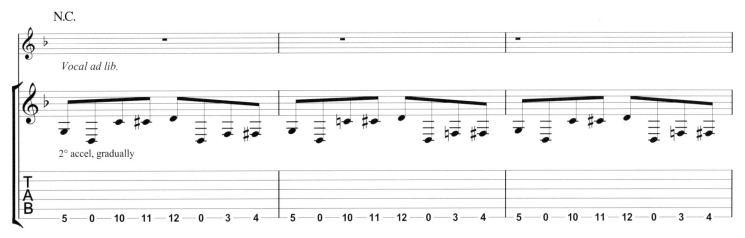

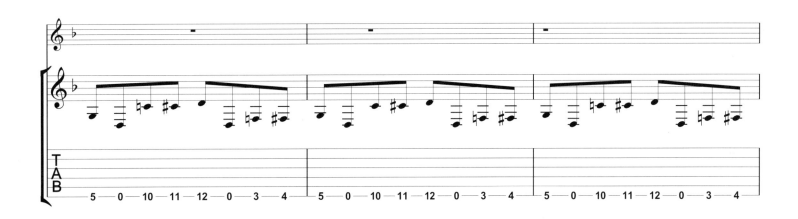

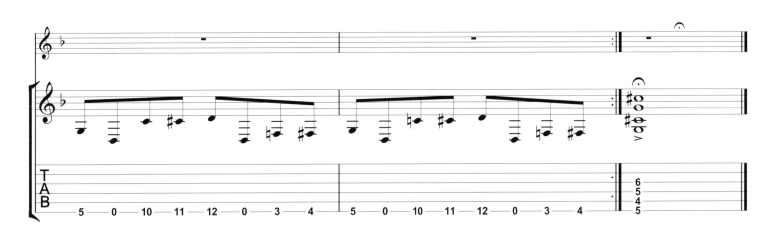

MAP OF YOUR HEAD

Lyrics & Music by Matthew Bellamy

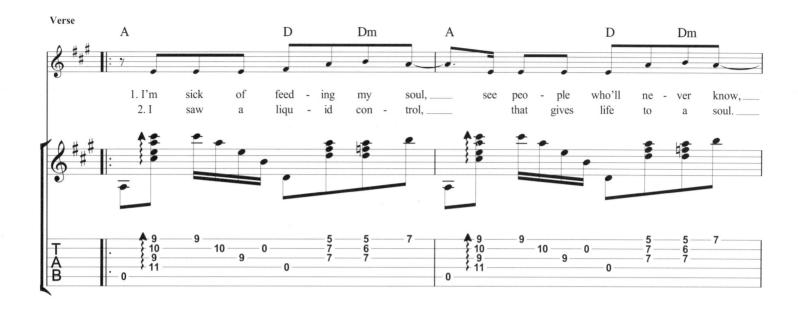

1. I'm sick of feed - ing my soul,____ see peo - ple who'll ne - ver know,____
2. I saw a liqu - id con - trol,____ that gives life to a soul.____

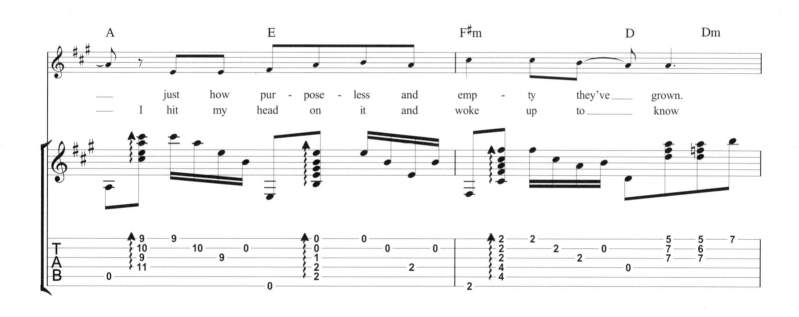

____ just how pur - pose - less and emp - ty they've____ grown.
____ I hit my head on it and woke up to _____ know

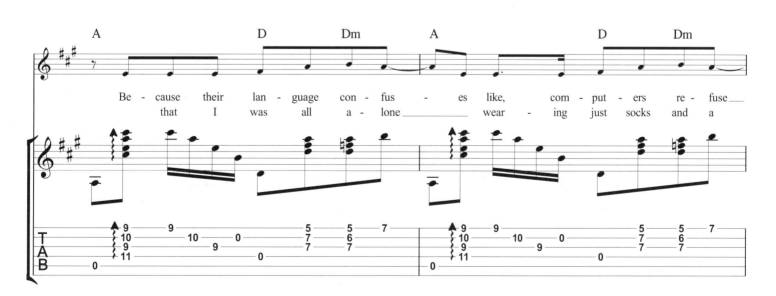

Be - cause their lan - guage con - fus - es like, com - put - ers re - fuse____
that I was all a - lone _____ wear - ing just socks and a

29

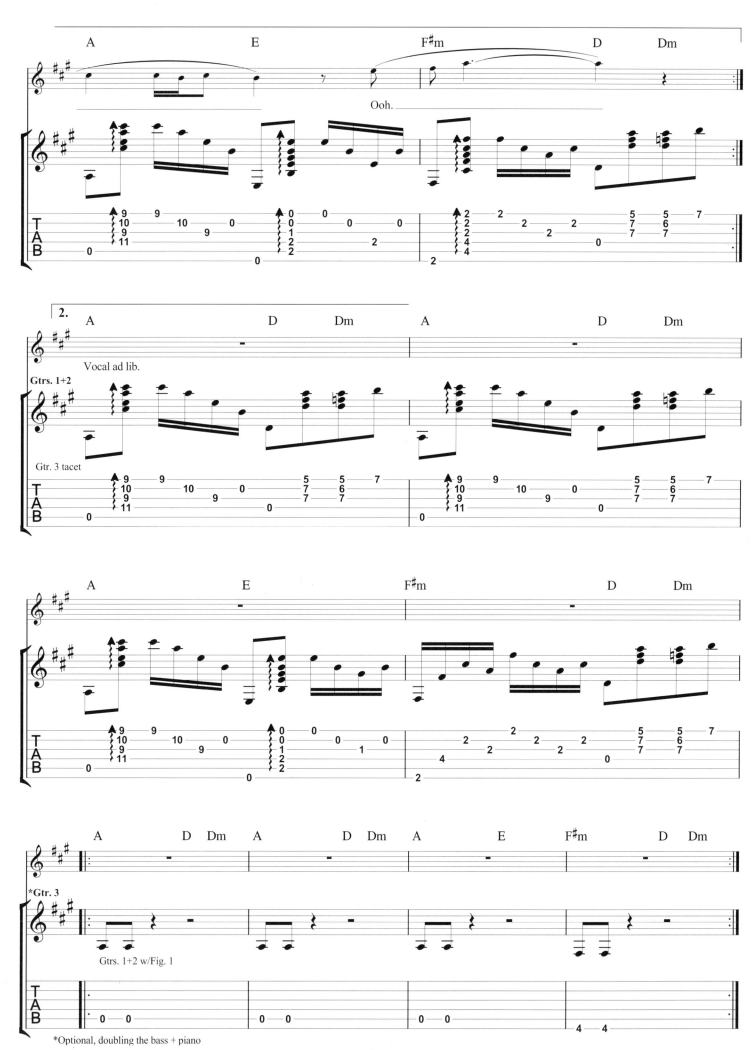

NATURE_1

Lyrics & Music by Matthew Bellamy

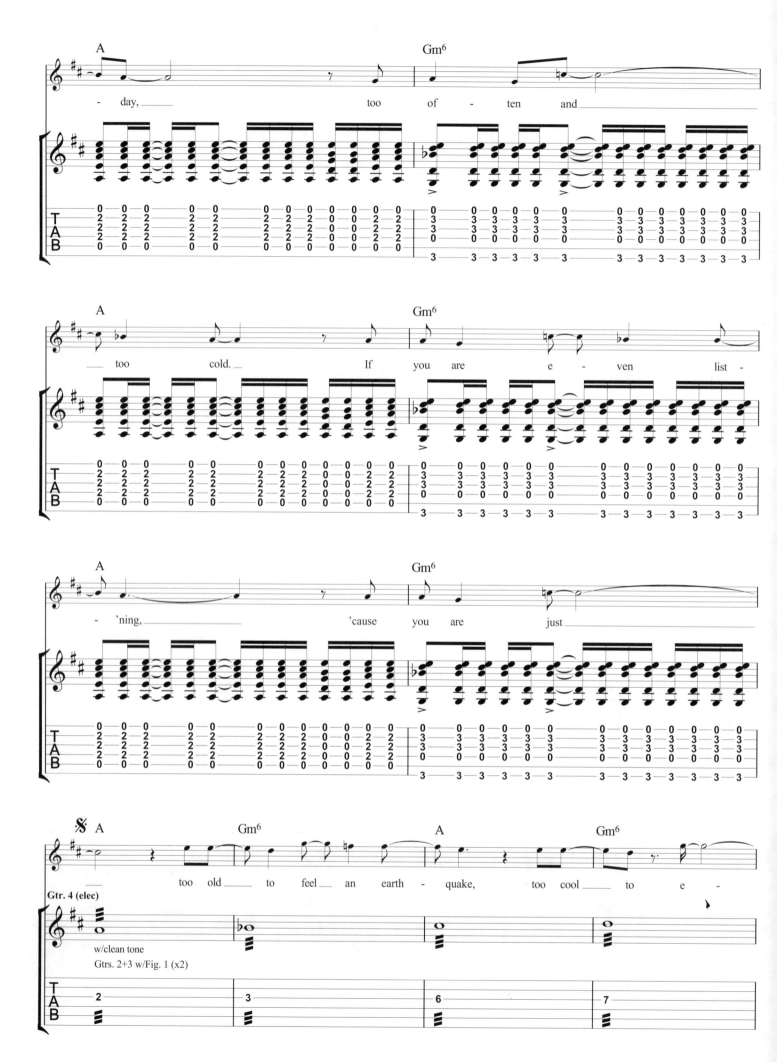

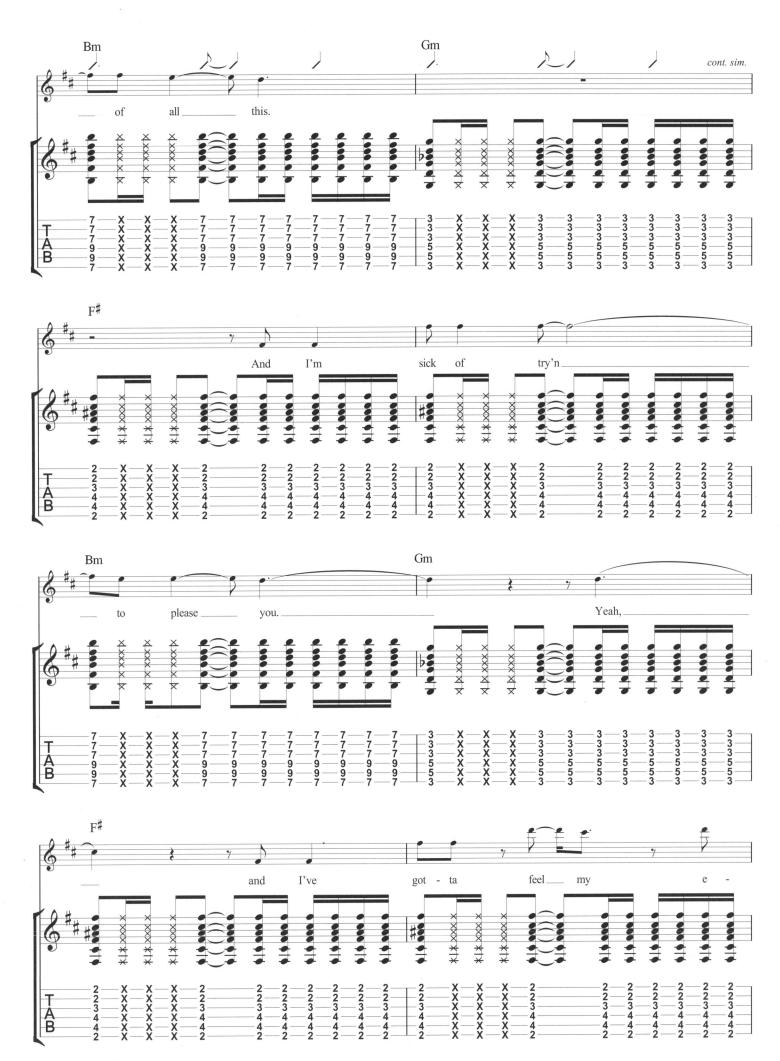

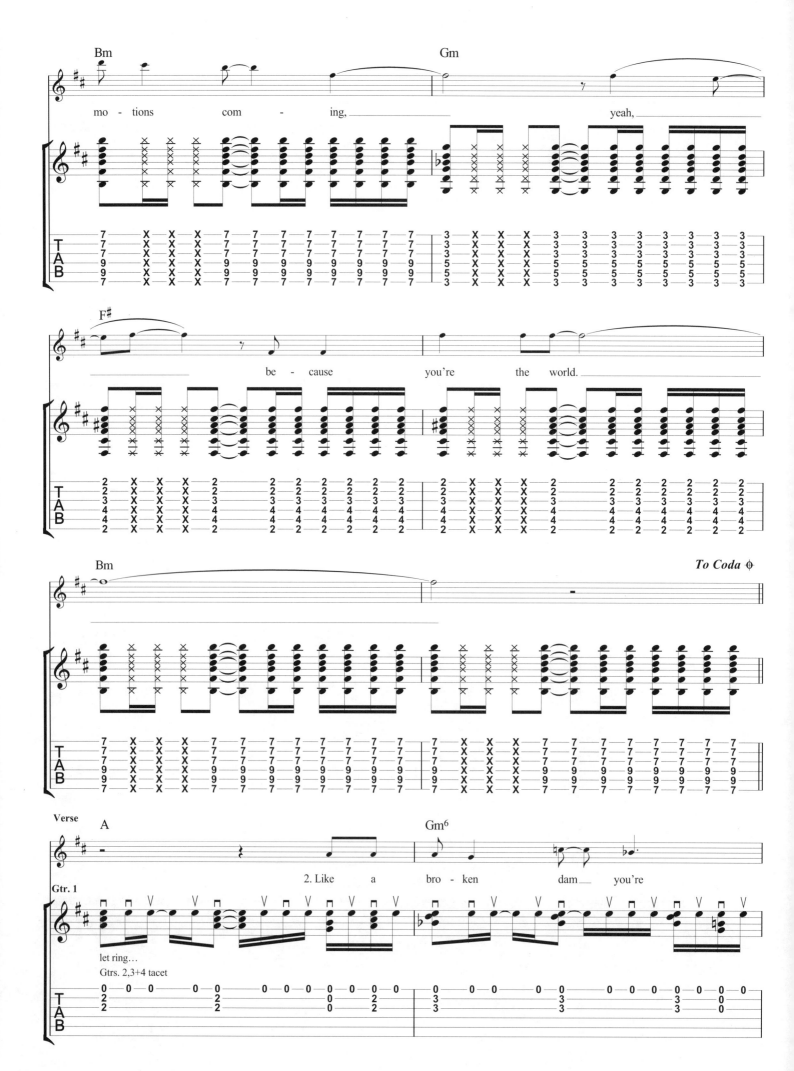

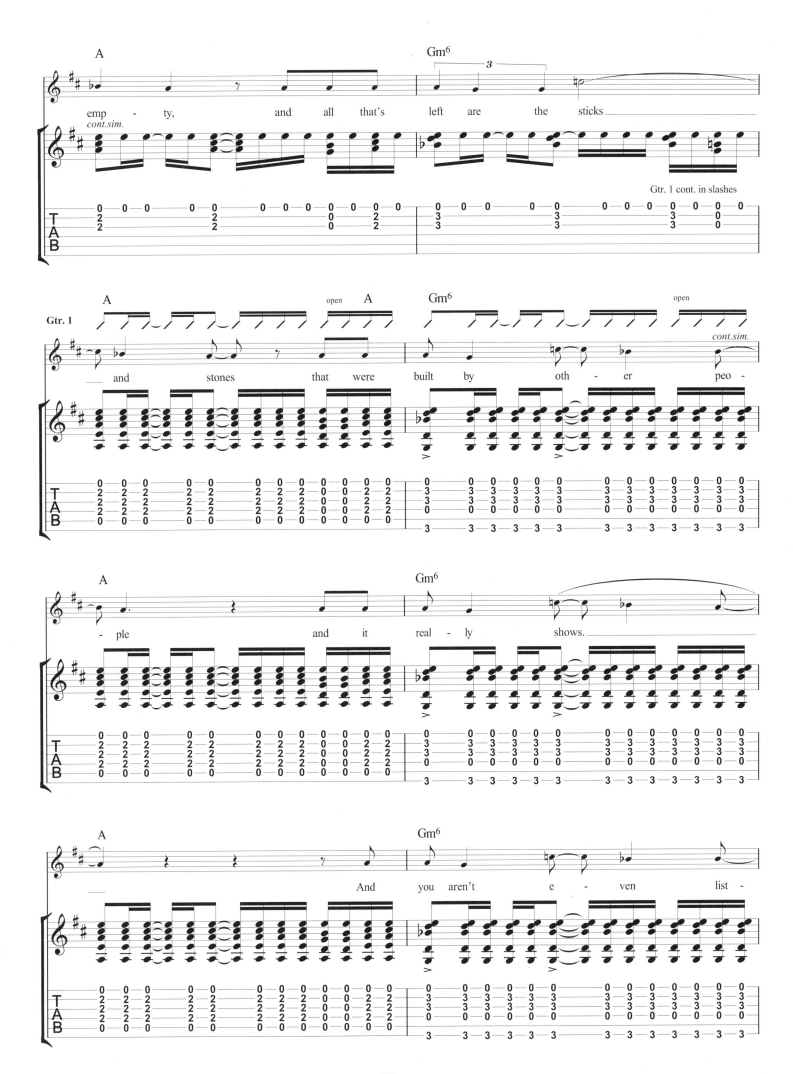

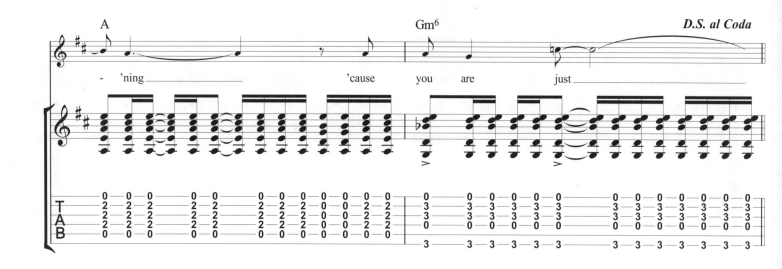

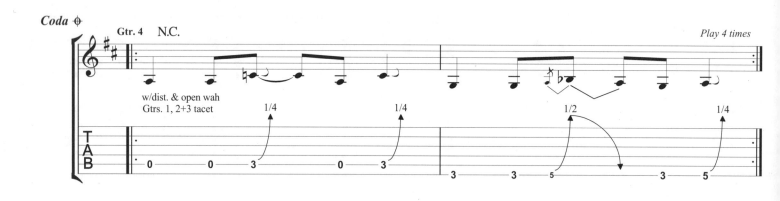

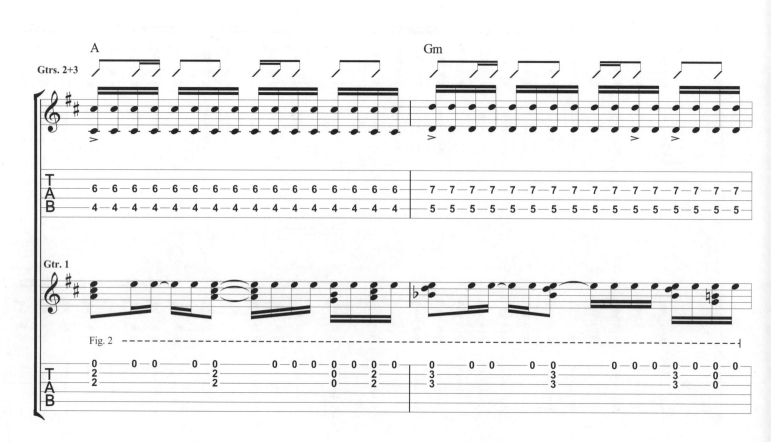

40

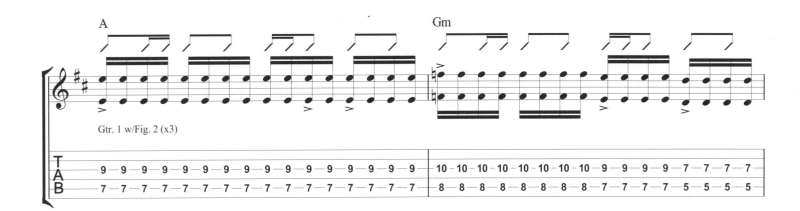

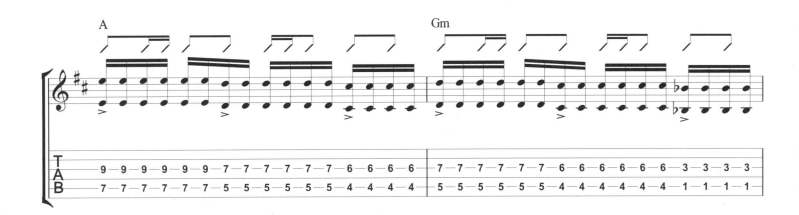

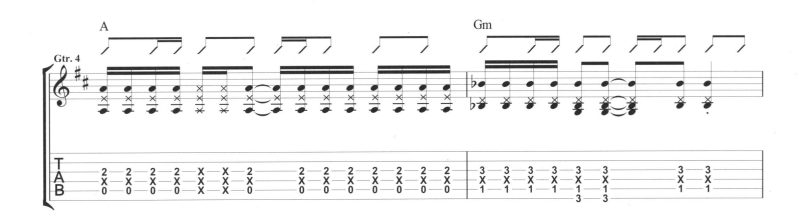

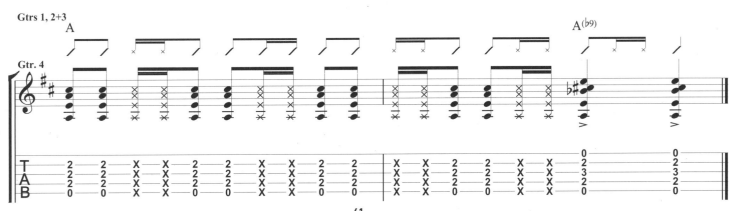

SHINE ACOUSTIC

Lyrics & Music by Matthew Bellamy

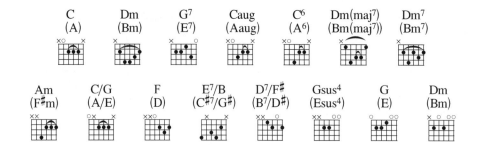

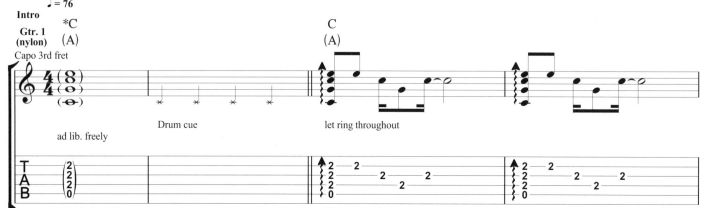

* Symbols in ( ) represent chord names with respect to capoed gtrs. (Tab 0 = 3rd fret)
  Symbols above represent actual sounding chords

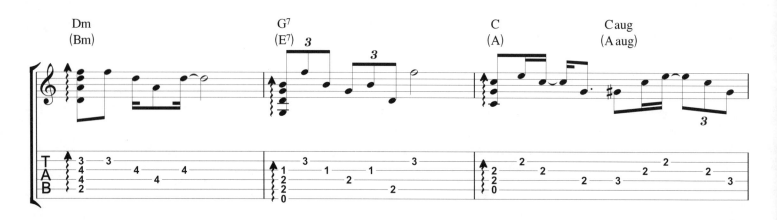

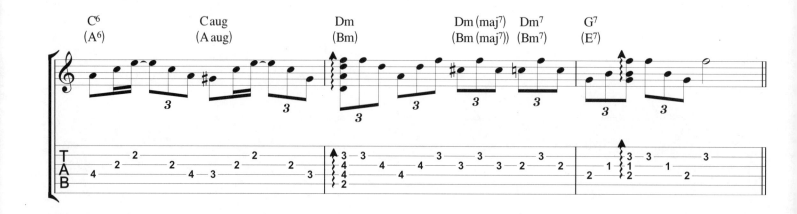

Verse

1. Whom ____ cares for the life we've
2. You can't cry now there's no - thing to

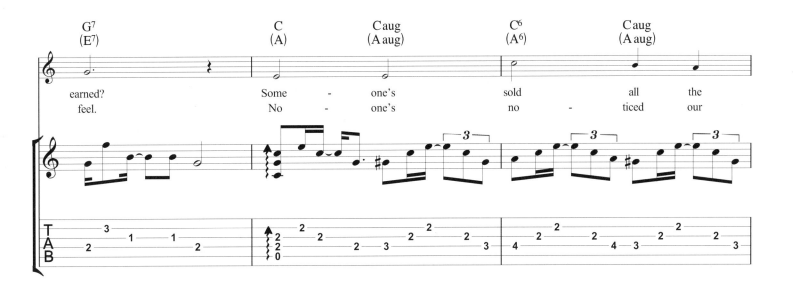

earned? Some - one's sold all the
feel. No - one's no - ticed our

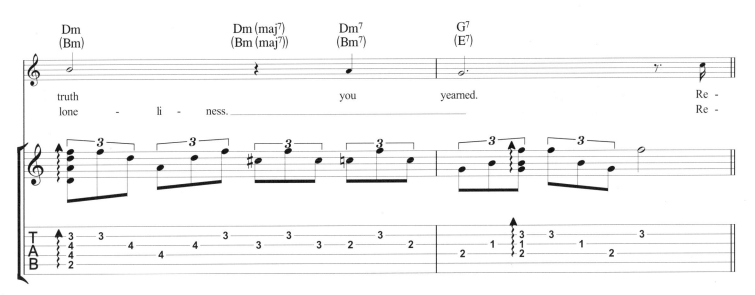

truth you yearned. Re -
lone - li - ness. ____ Re -

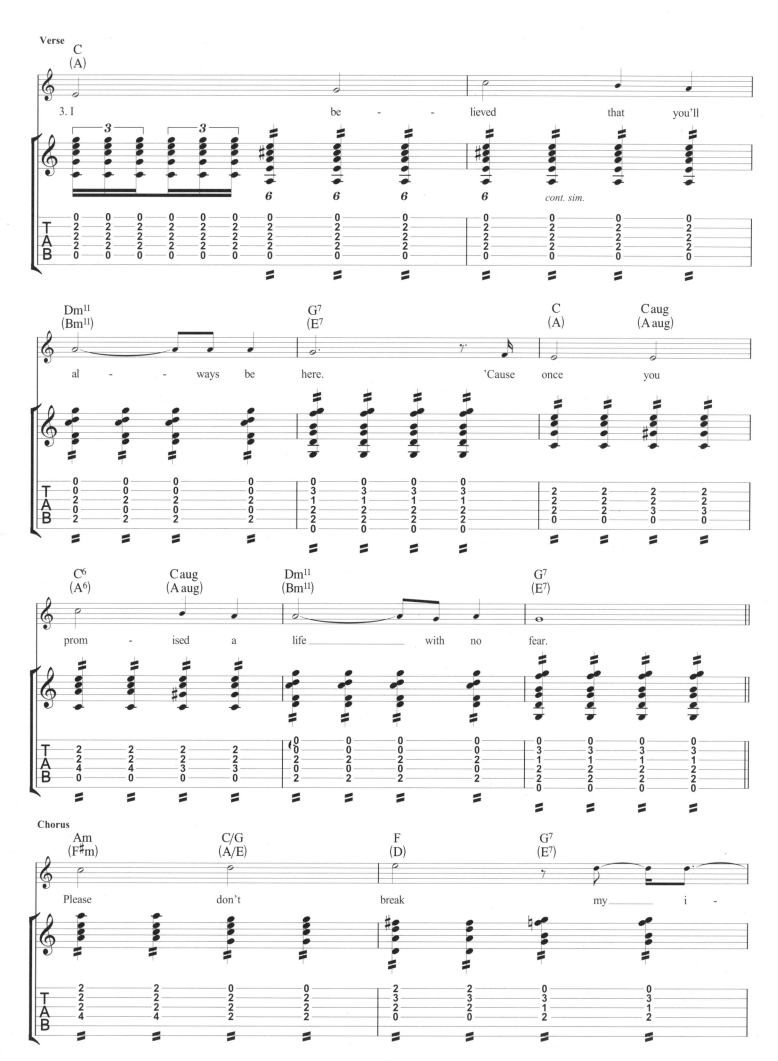

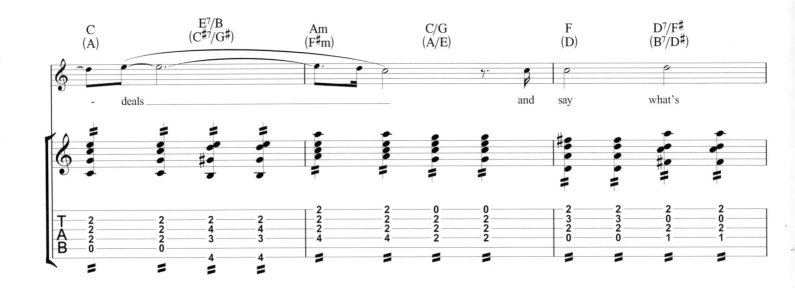

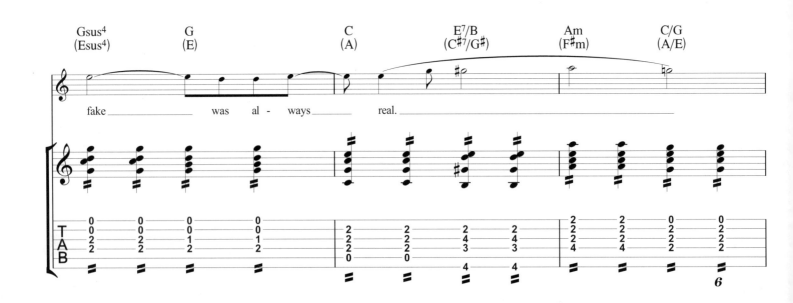

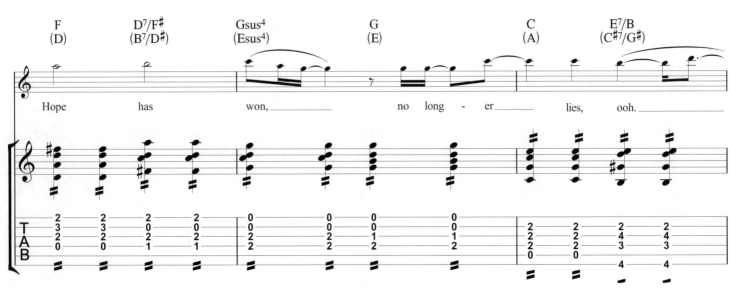

46

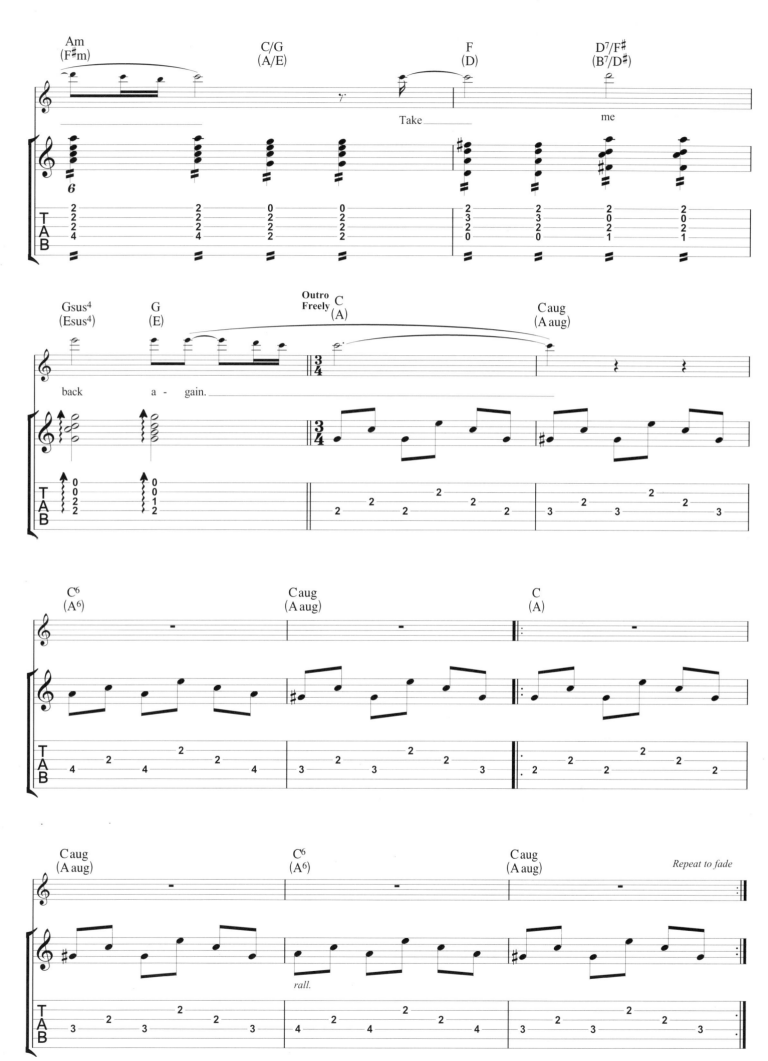

ASHAMED

Lyrics & Music by Matthew Bellamy

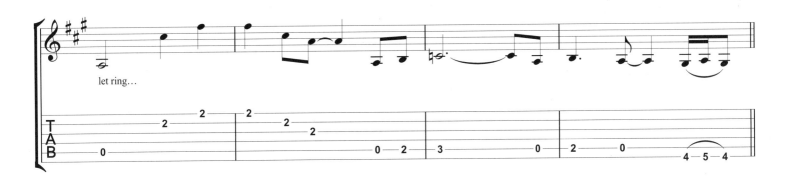

1. I know there's some-thing that you're dyin' to tell me,
2. There's al-ways some-thing that makes you guil-ty.

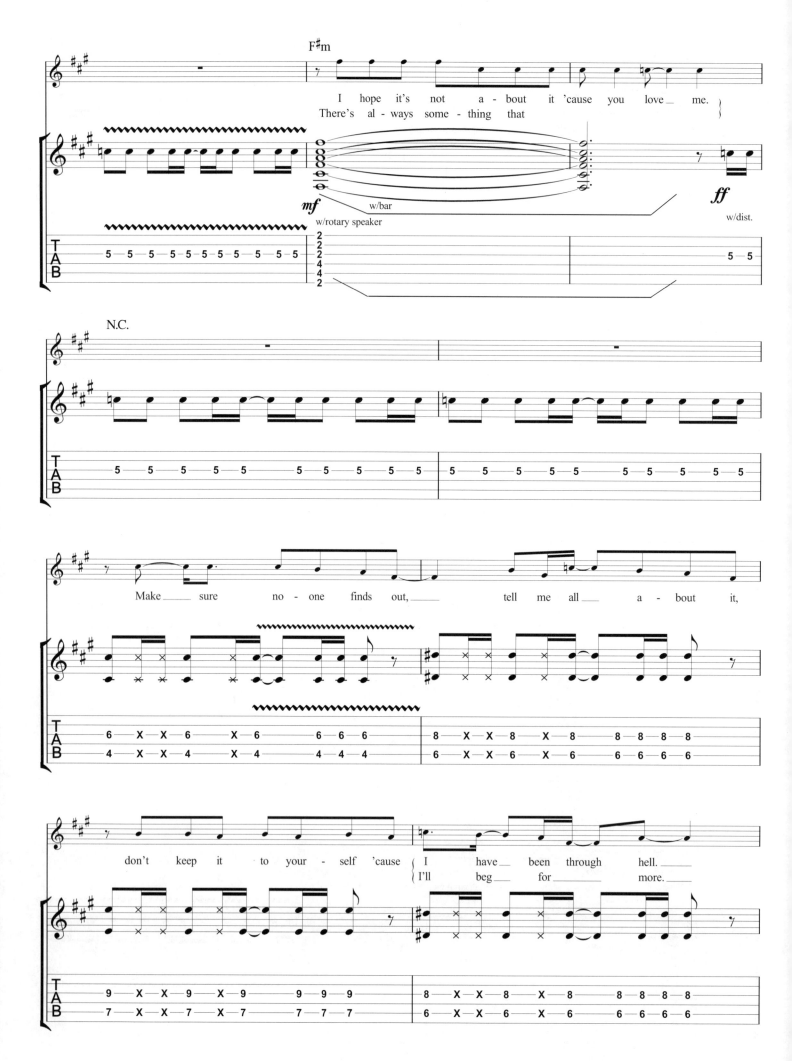

50

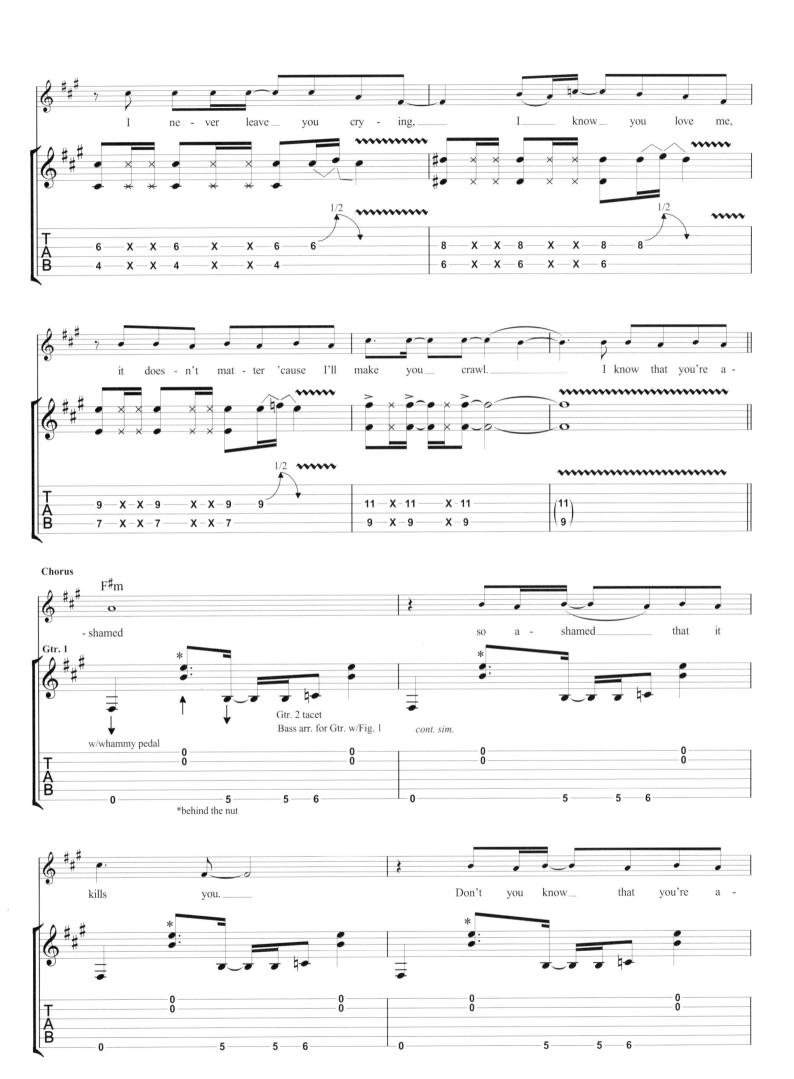

-shamed?　　So　much　that　it　kills　　　you.

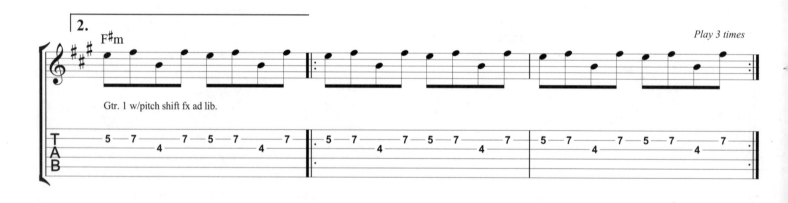

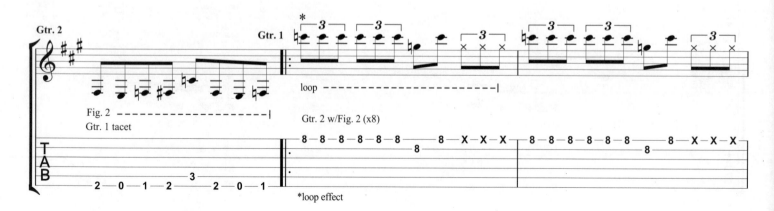

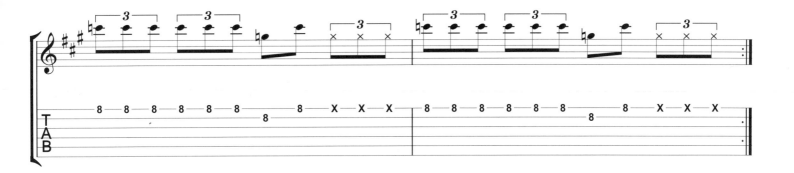

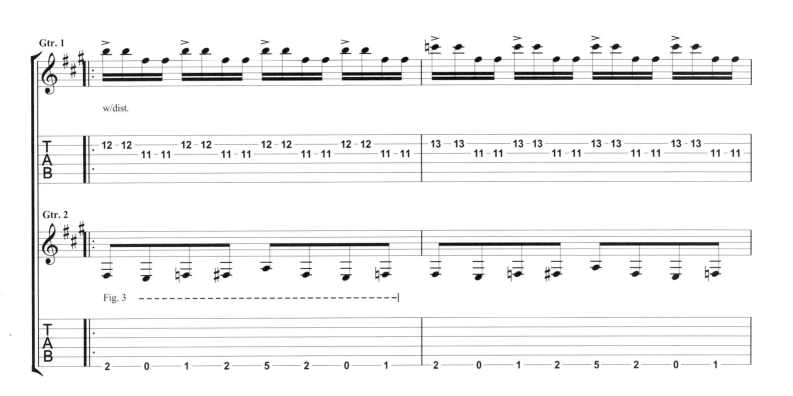

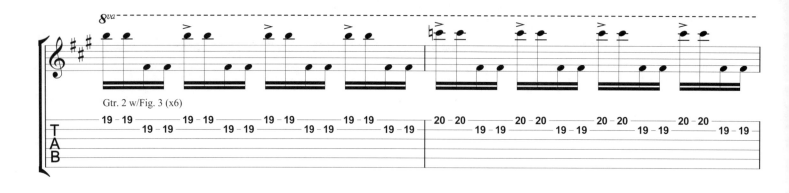

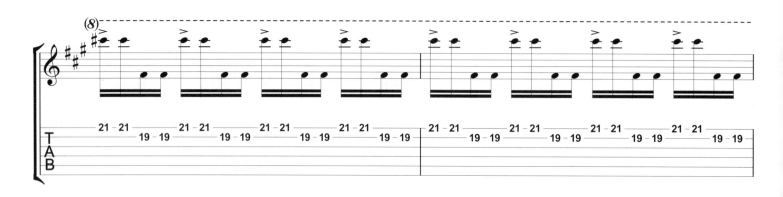

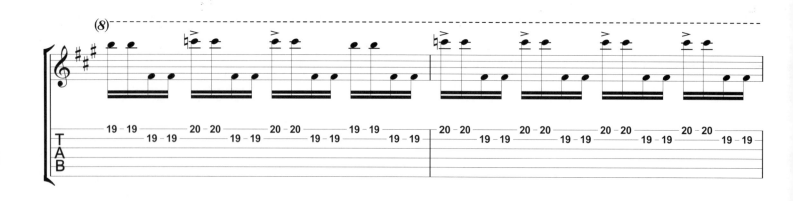

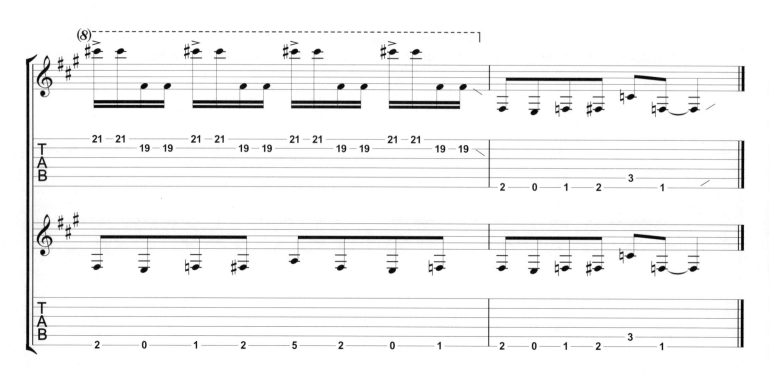

THE GALLERY

Music by Matthew Bellamy

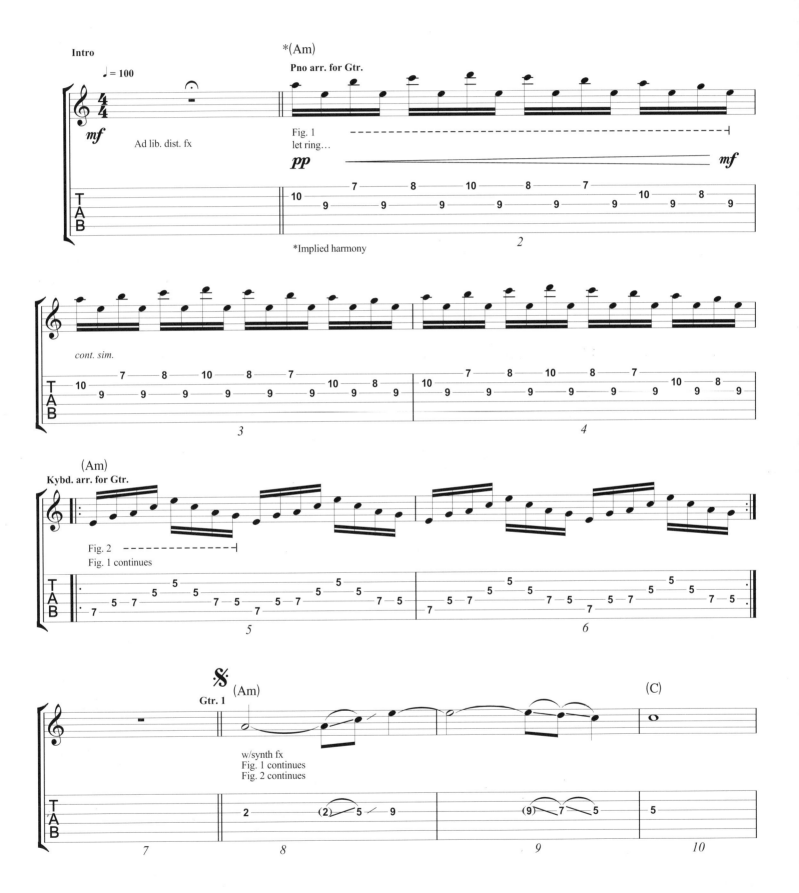

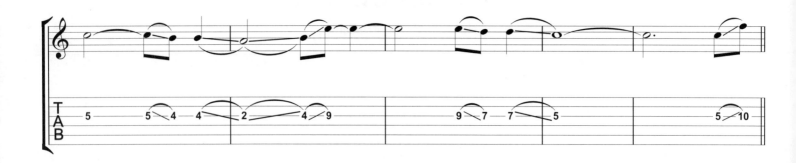

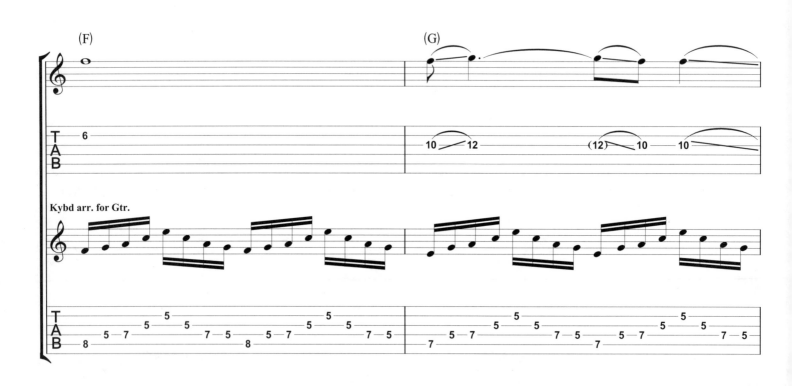

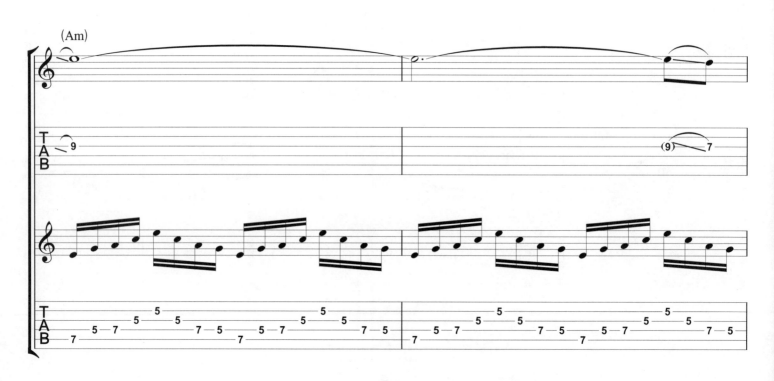

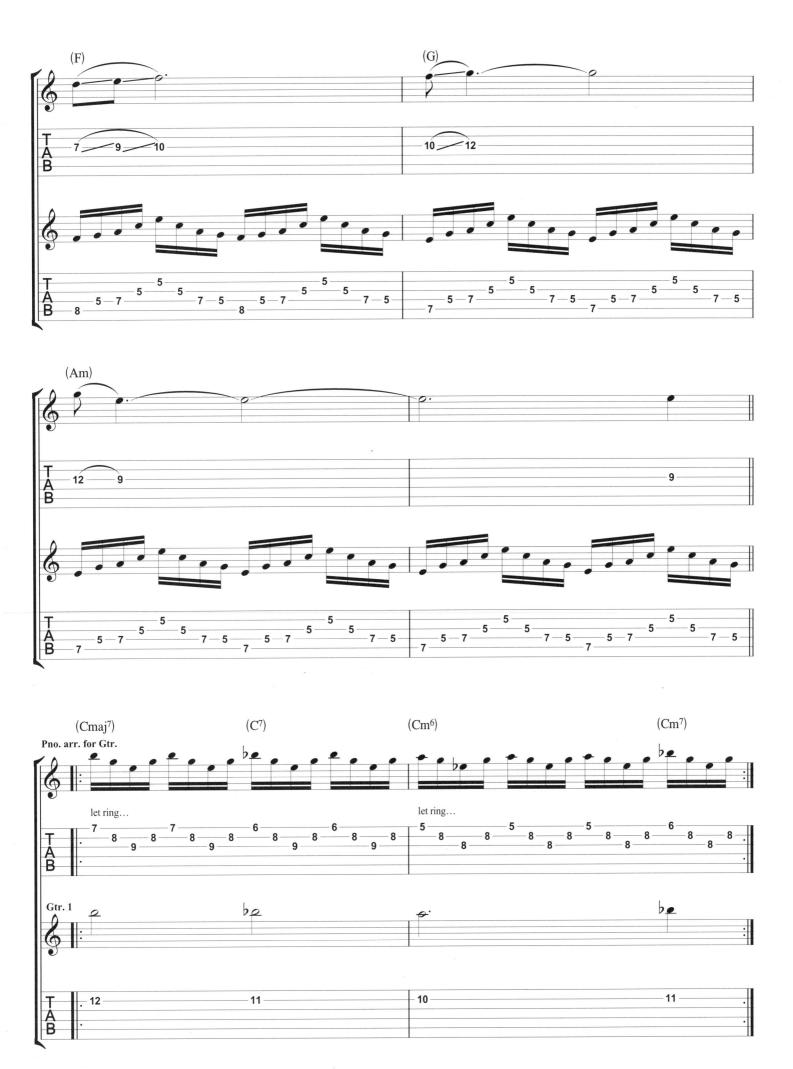

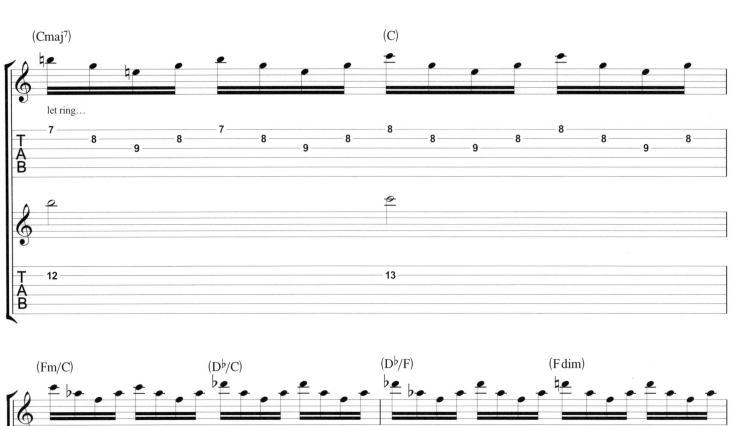

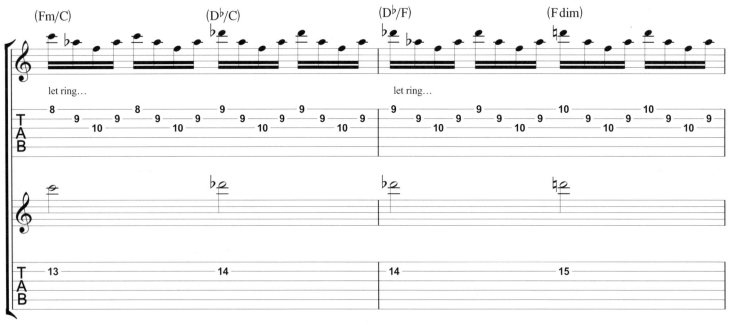

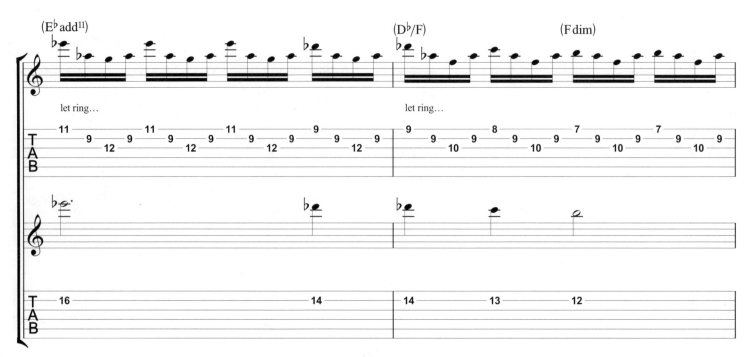

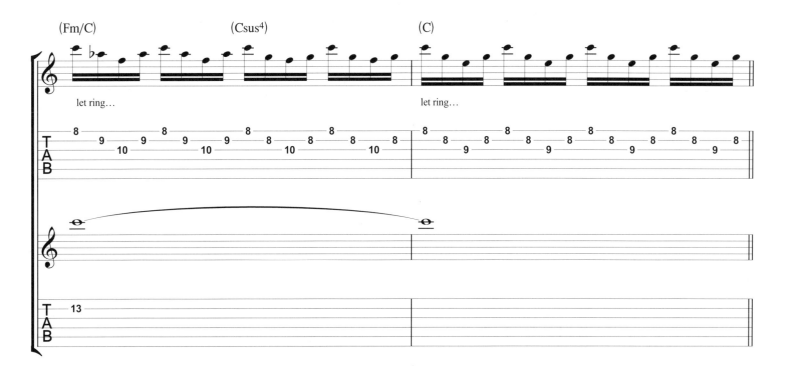

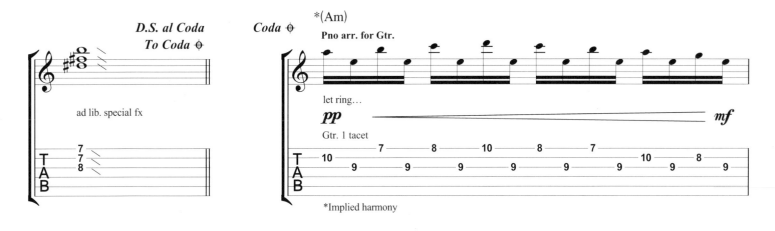

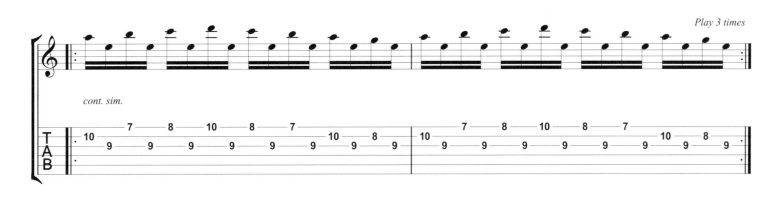

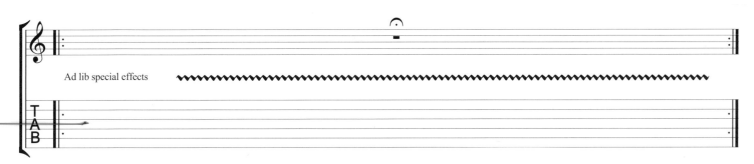

HYPER CHONDRIAC MUSIC

Lyrics & Music by Matthew Bellamy

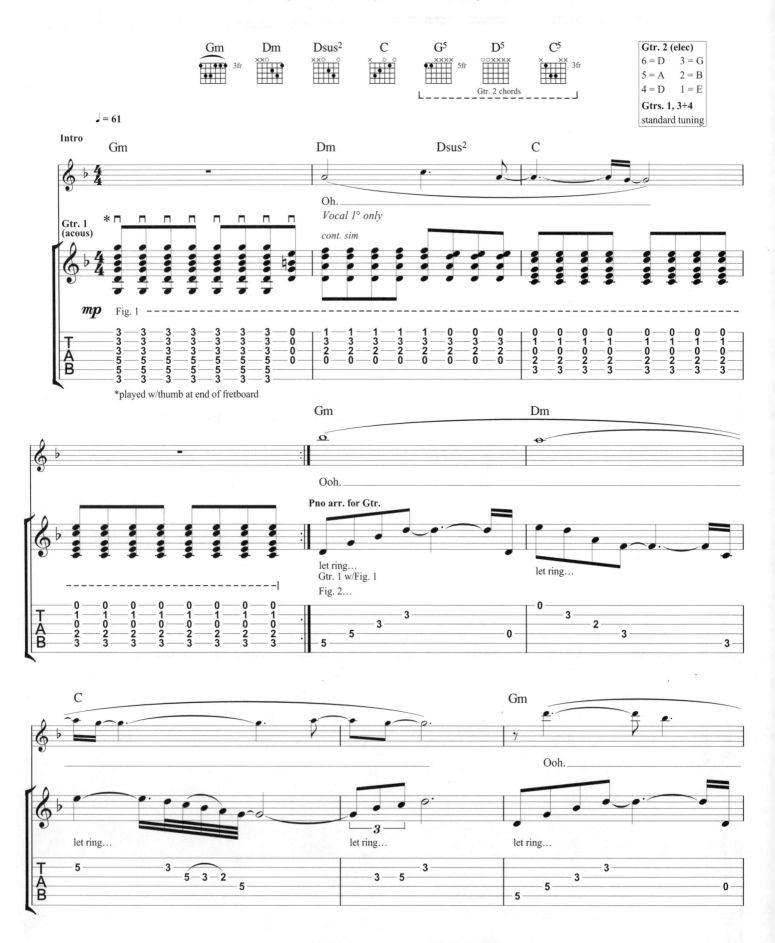

*played w/thumb at end of fretboard

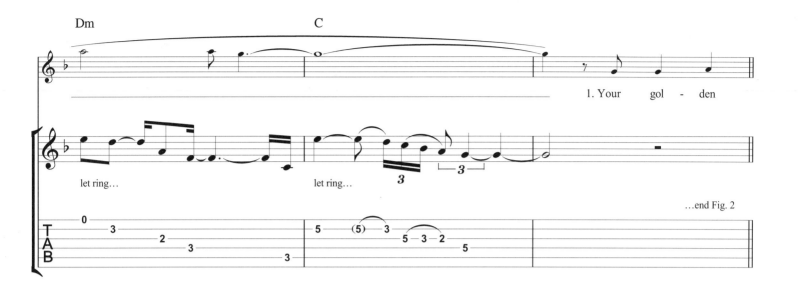

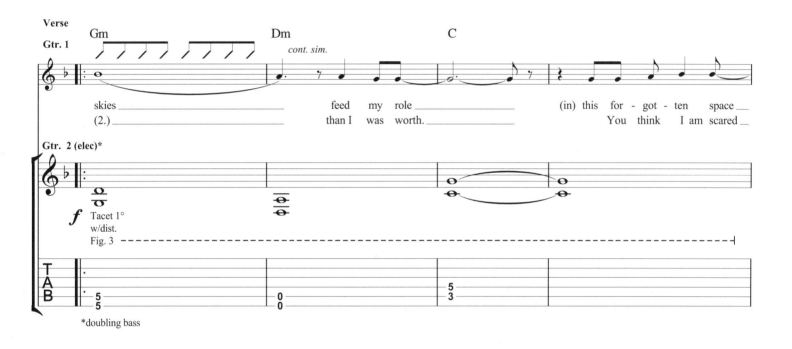

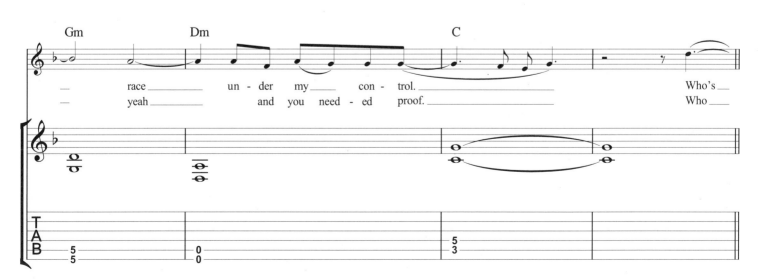

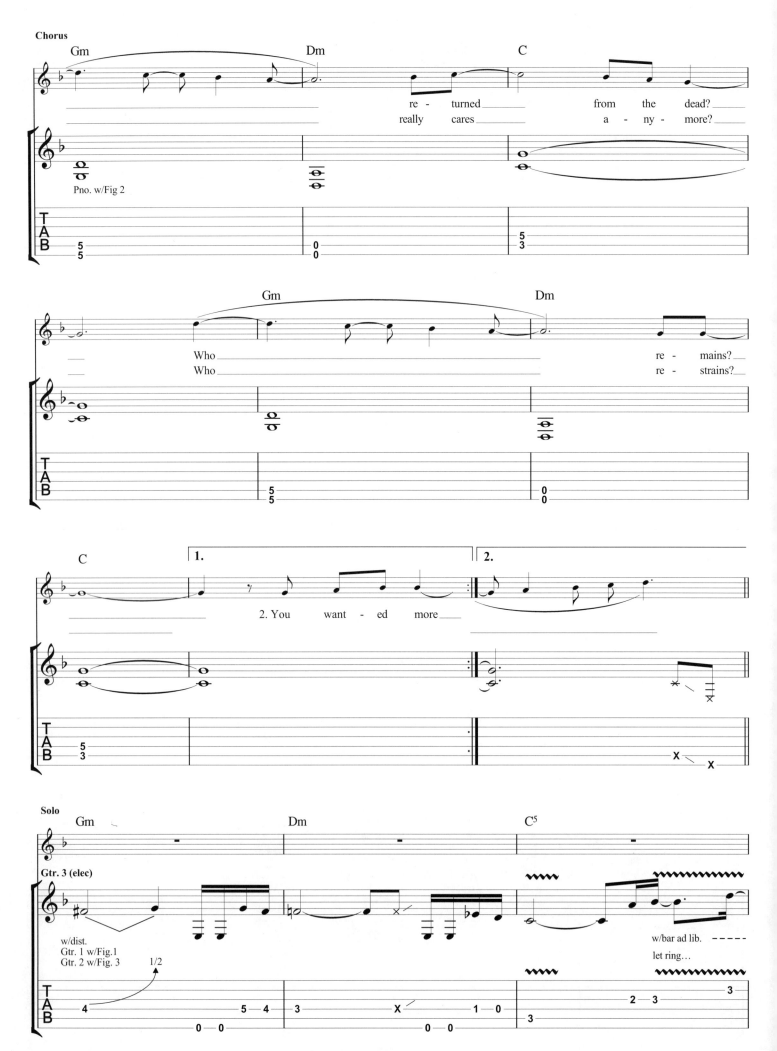

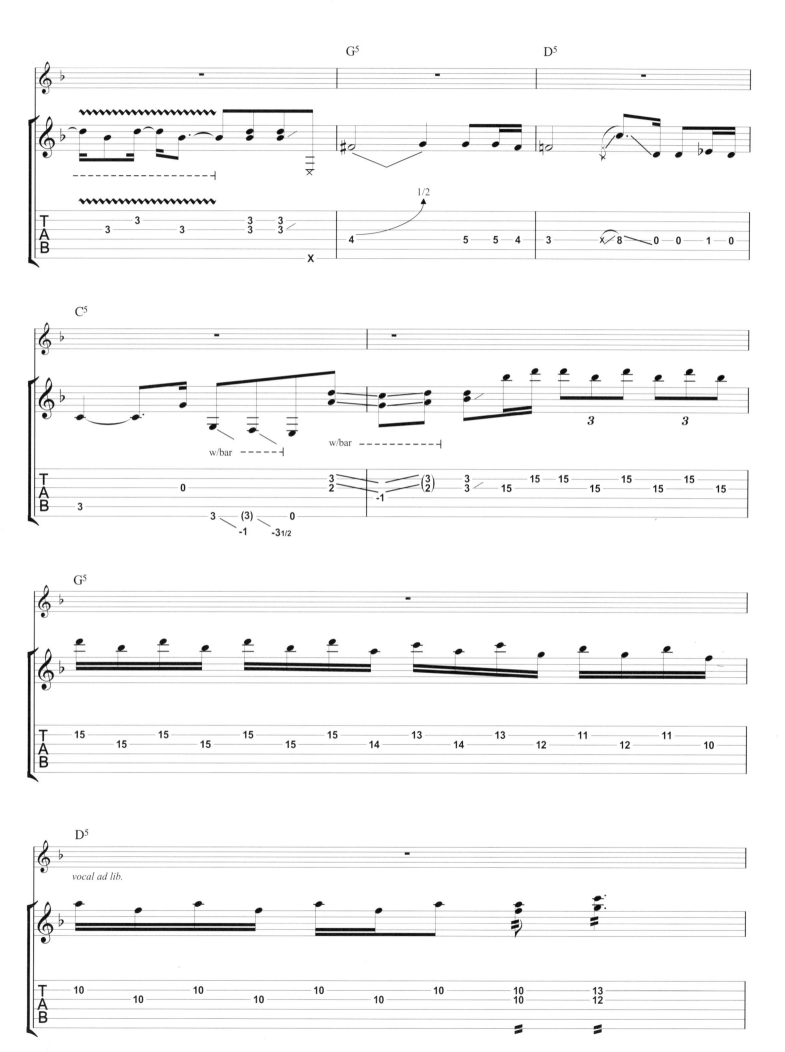

64

-ver did. I don't love you

I ne - ver will.

DEAD STAR

Lyrics & Music by Matthew Bellamy

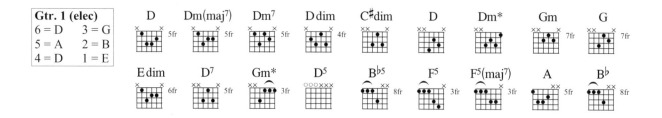

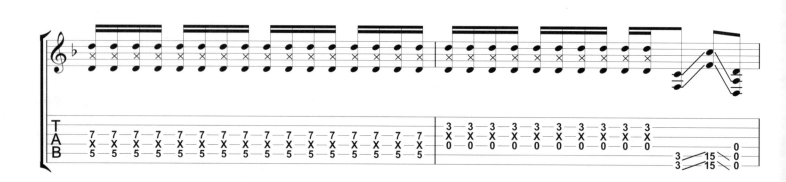

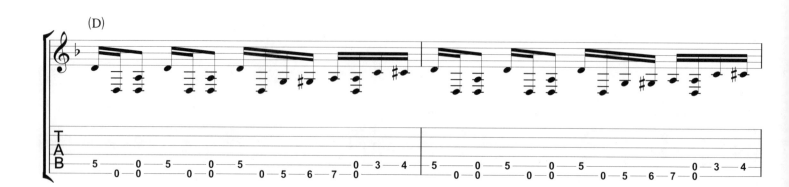

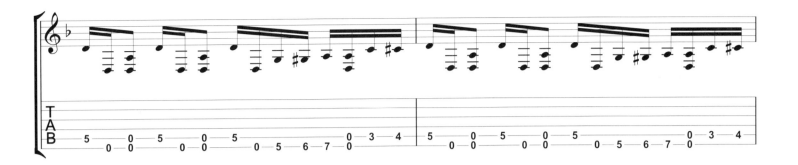

Verse

1. Shame on you for think - ing
2. Shame on you for think - ing

mf w/slight dist.
let ring…

(optional)

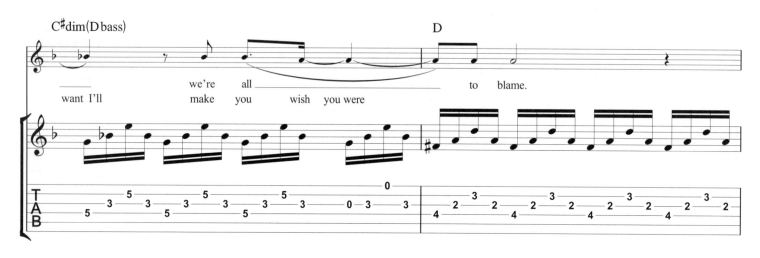

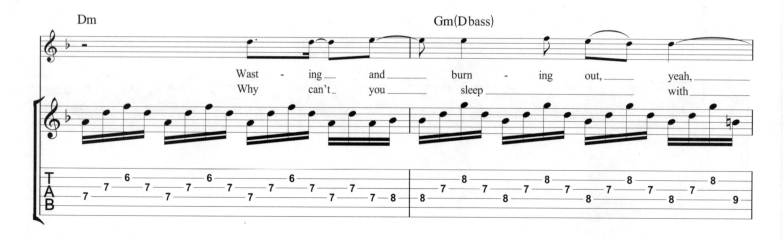

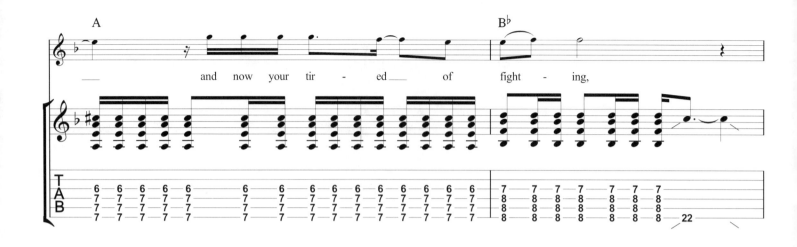

and now your tir - ed____ of fight - ing,

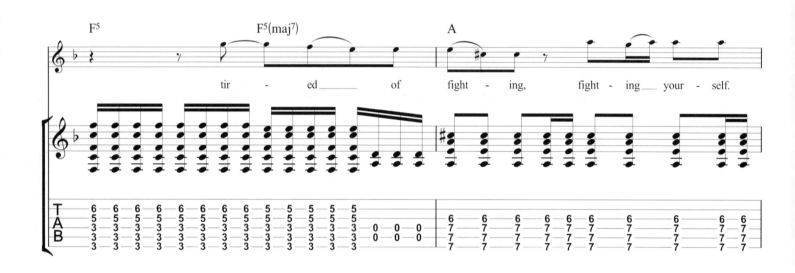

tir - ed____ of fight - ing, fight - ing____ your - self.

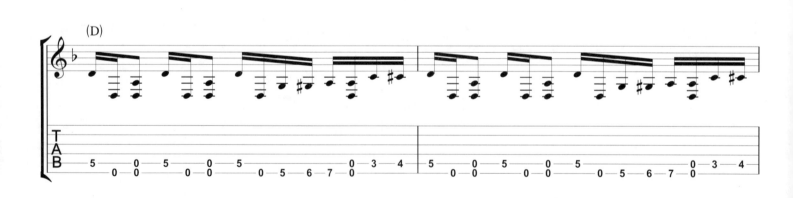

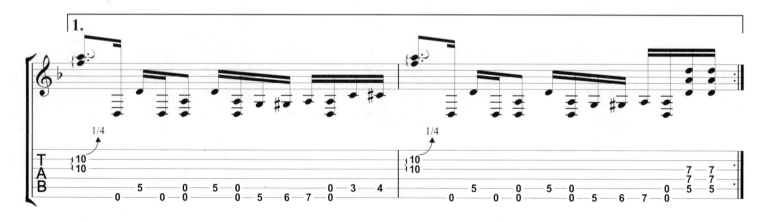

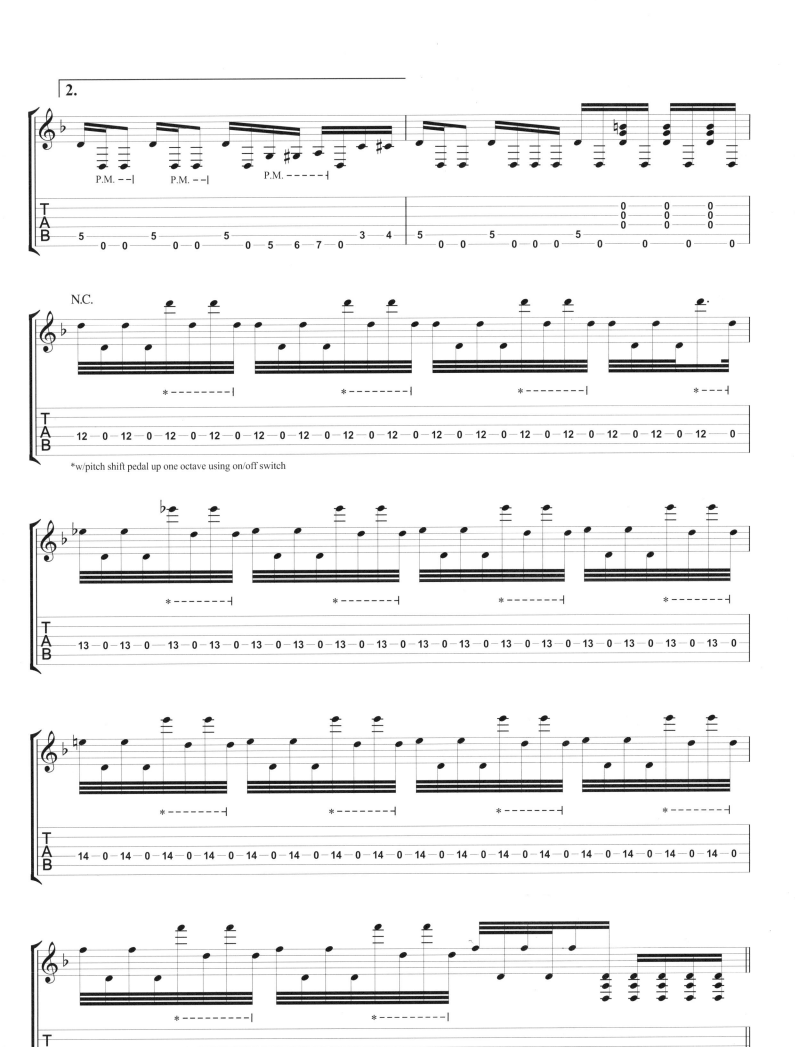

*w/pitch shift pedal up one octave using on/off switch

MICRO CUTS

Lyrics & Music by Matthew Bellamy

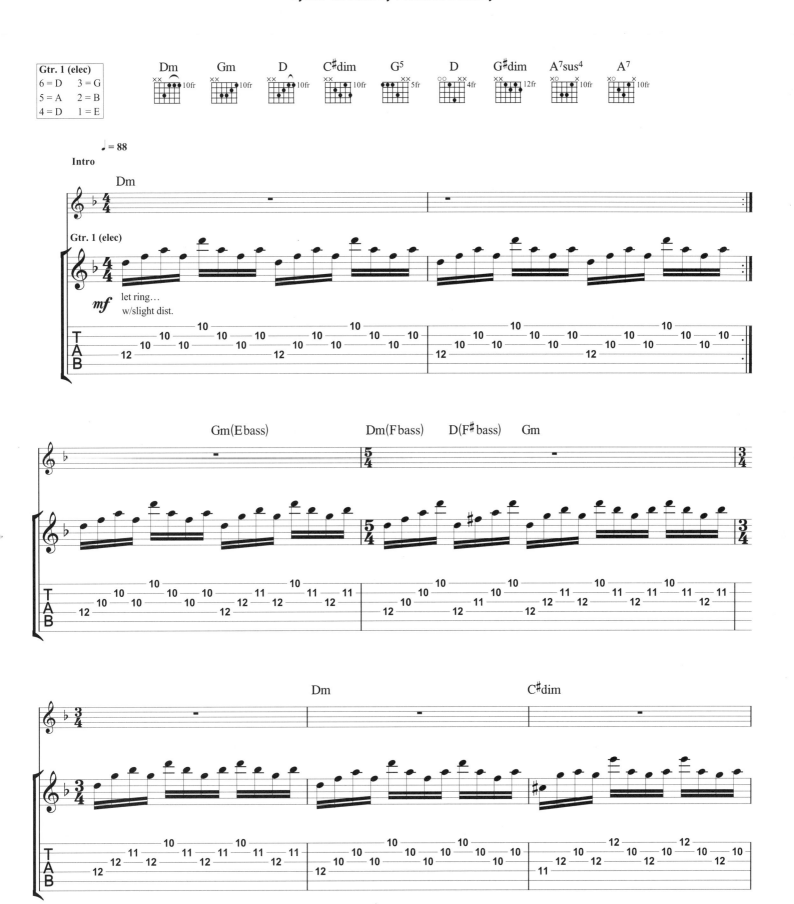

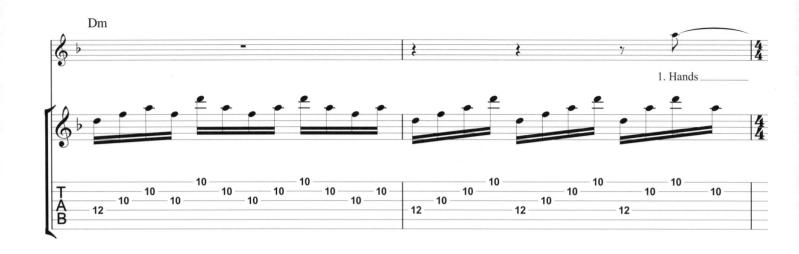

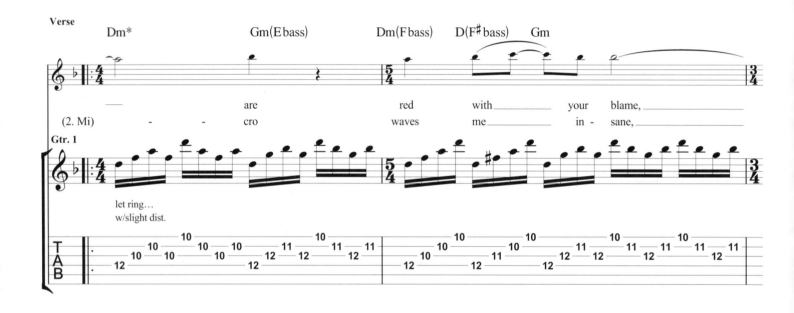

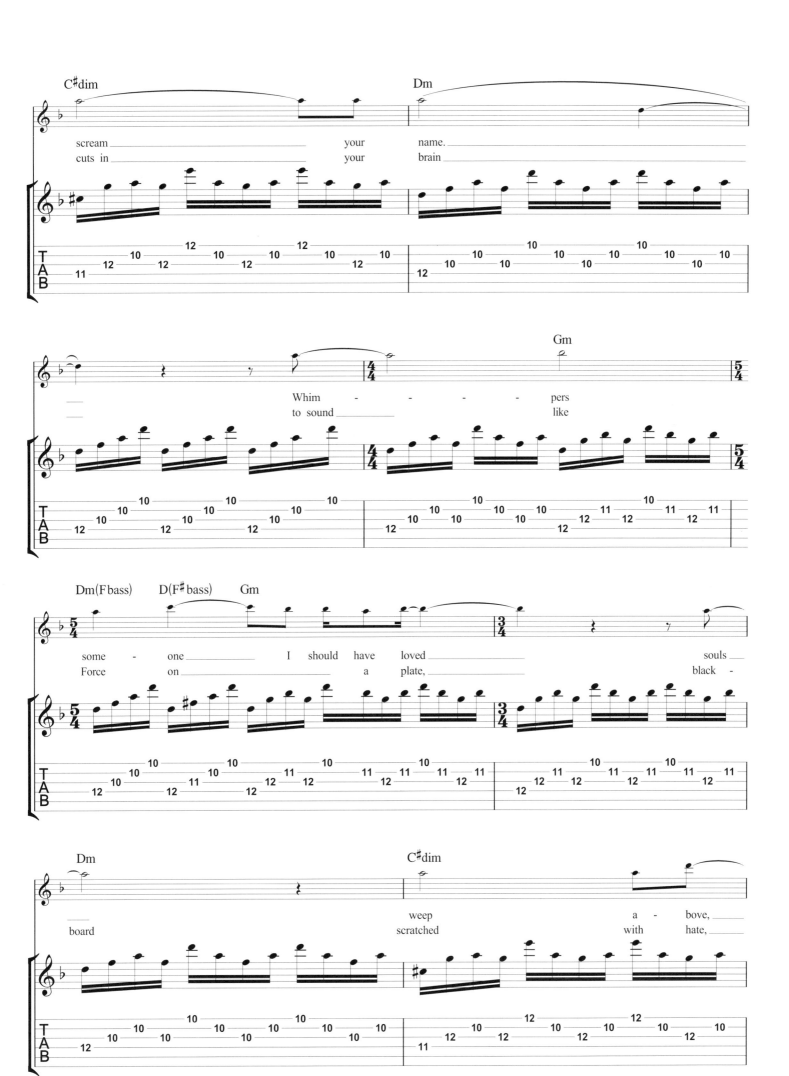

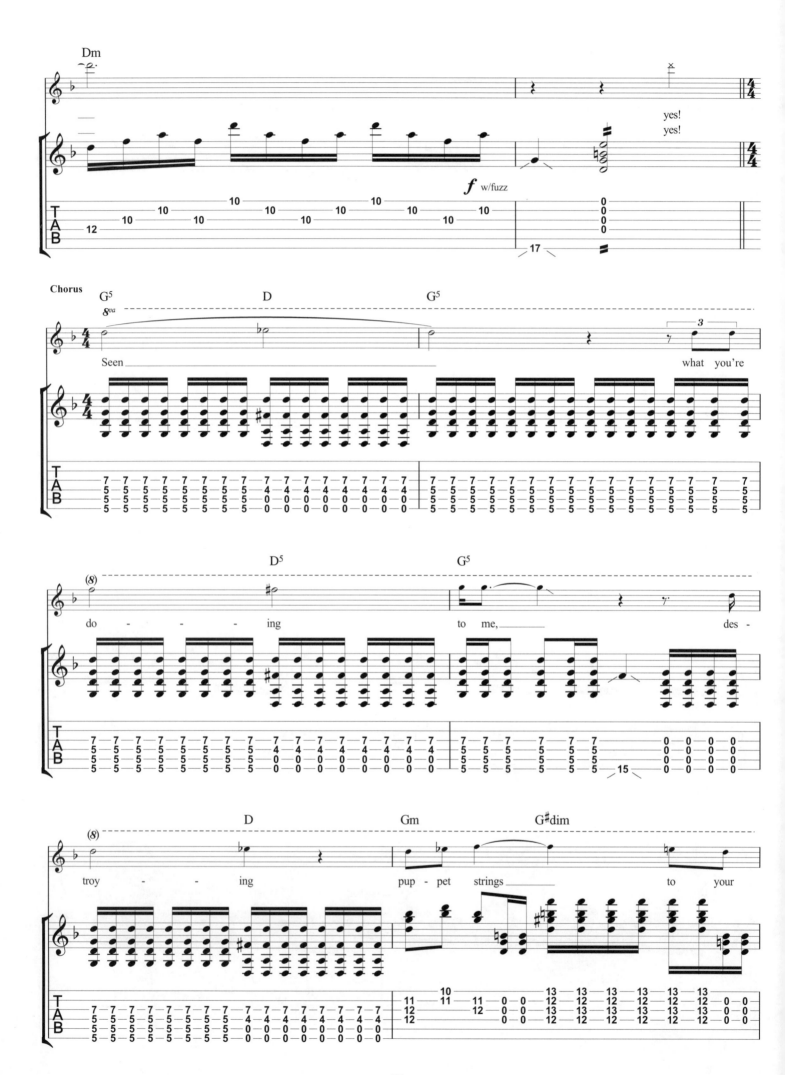

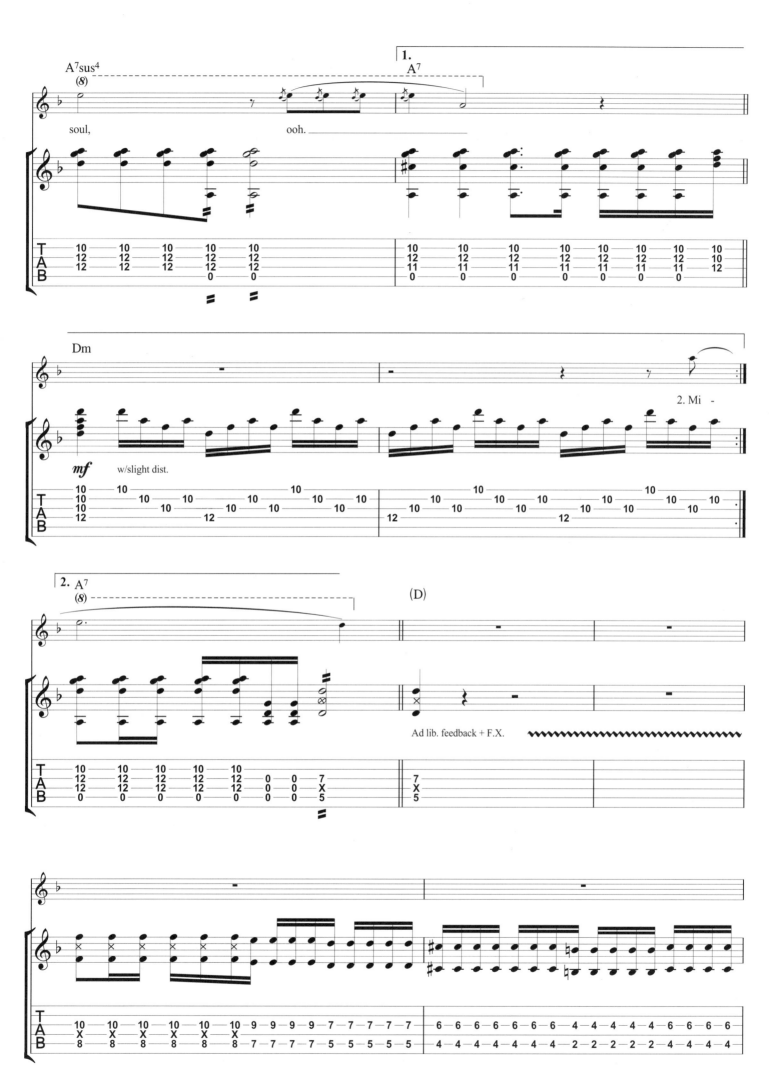

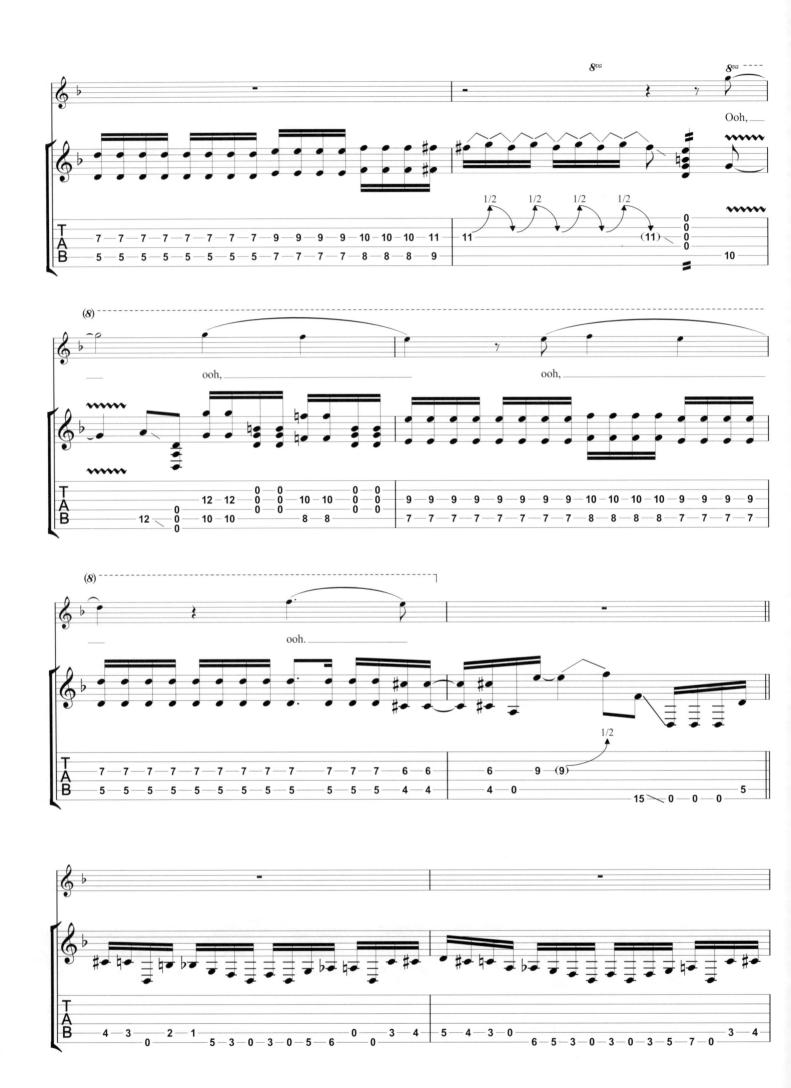

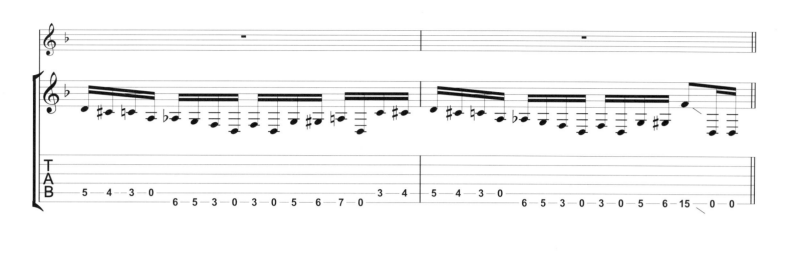

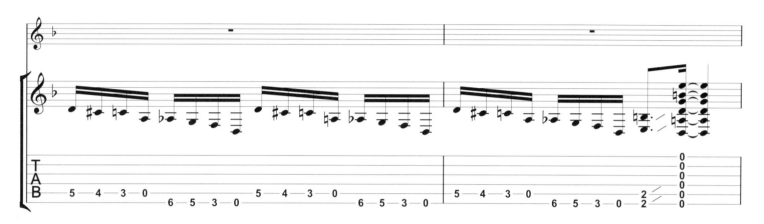

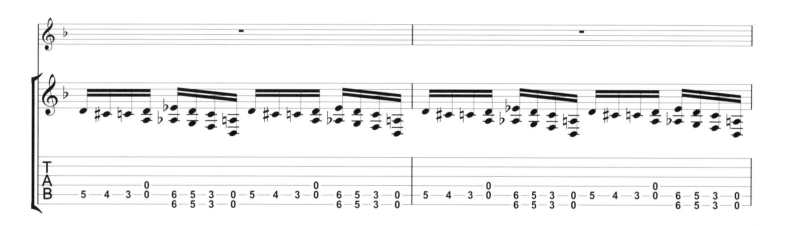

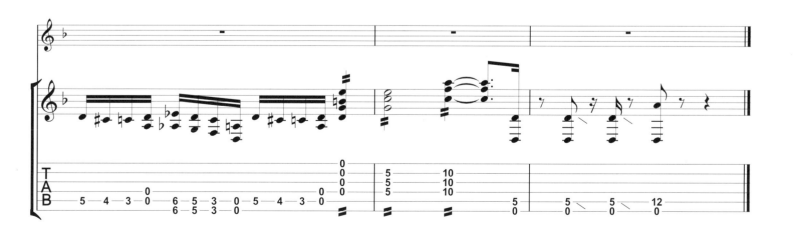

CITIZEN ERASED

Lyrics & Music by Matthew Bellamy

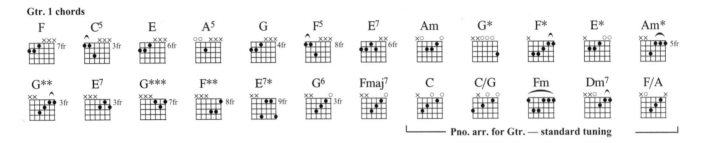

Originally played on a 7 string Mansun guitar tuned:

7 = A, 6 = A, 5 = D, 4 = D, 3 = G, 2 = B, 1 = E, where the 5th and 4th are unisons and 7th and 6th are in octaves.

For convenience it has been adapted here for a 6 string guitar tuned:

6 = A, 5 = A, 4 = D, 3 = G, 2 = B, 1 = E, where the 6th and 5th are in octaves.

(For seven string chord shapes, play same note (if fretted) on the 4th & 5th strings)

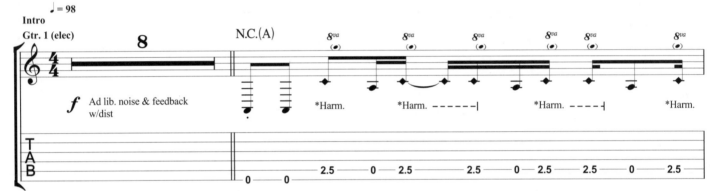

*Play open harmonic between 2nd & 3rd frets

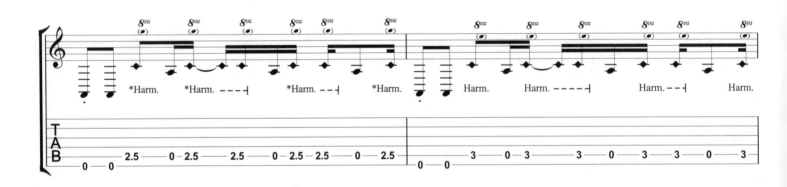

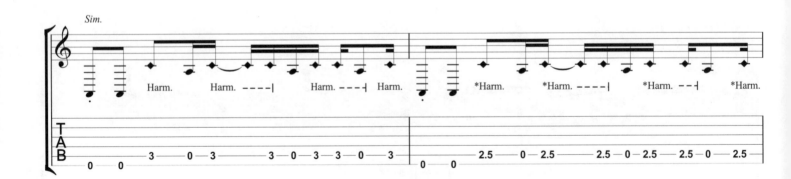

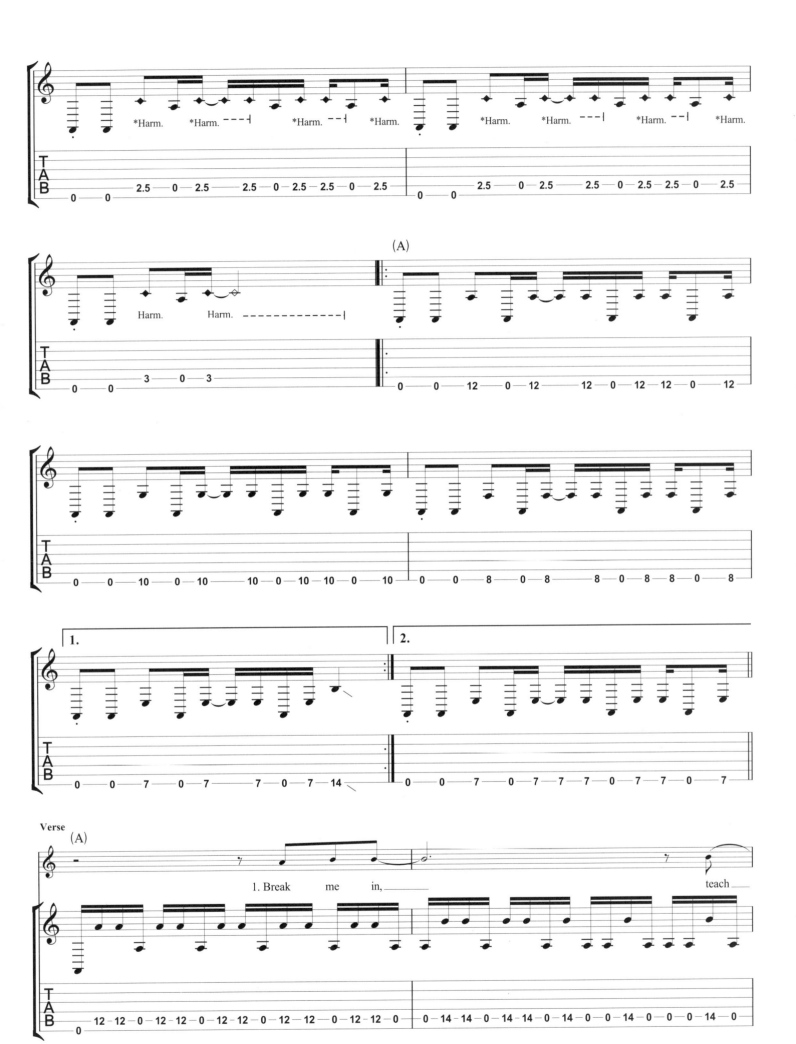

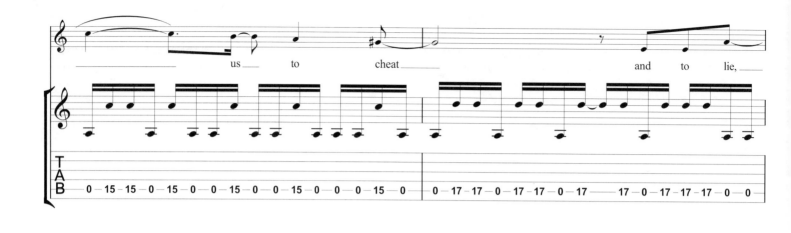

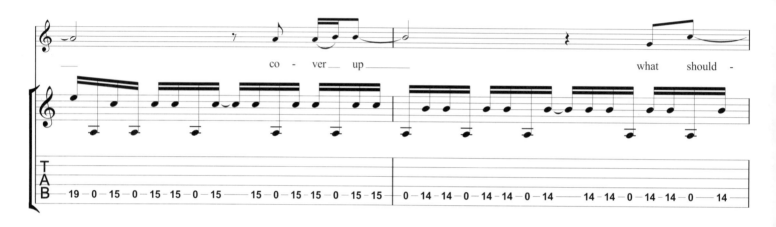

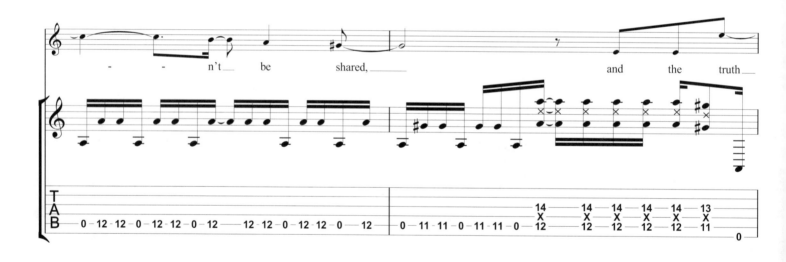

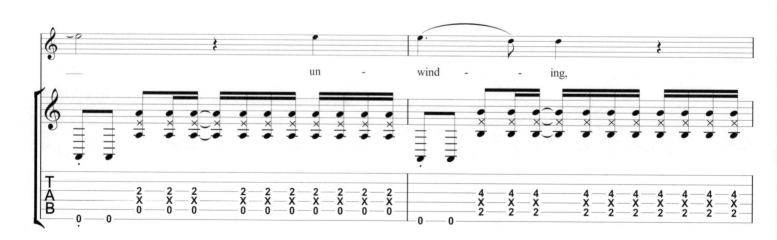

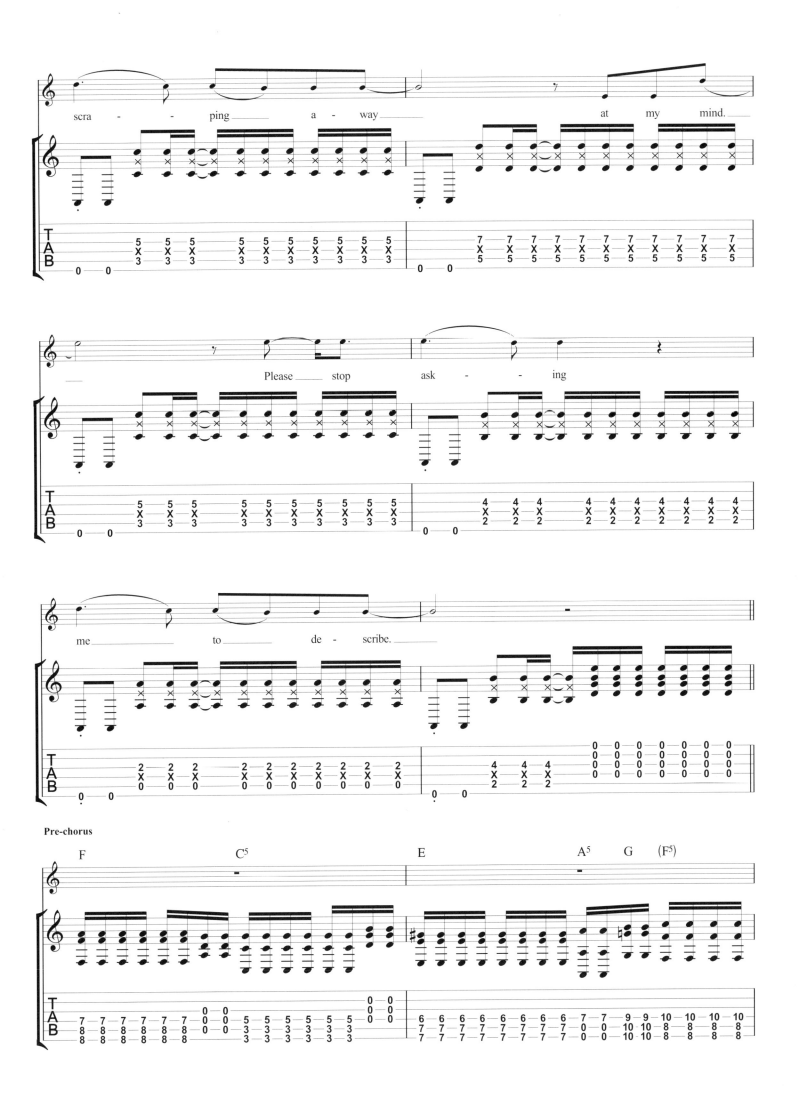

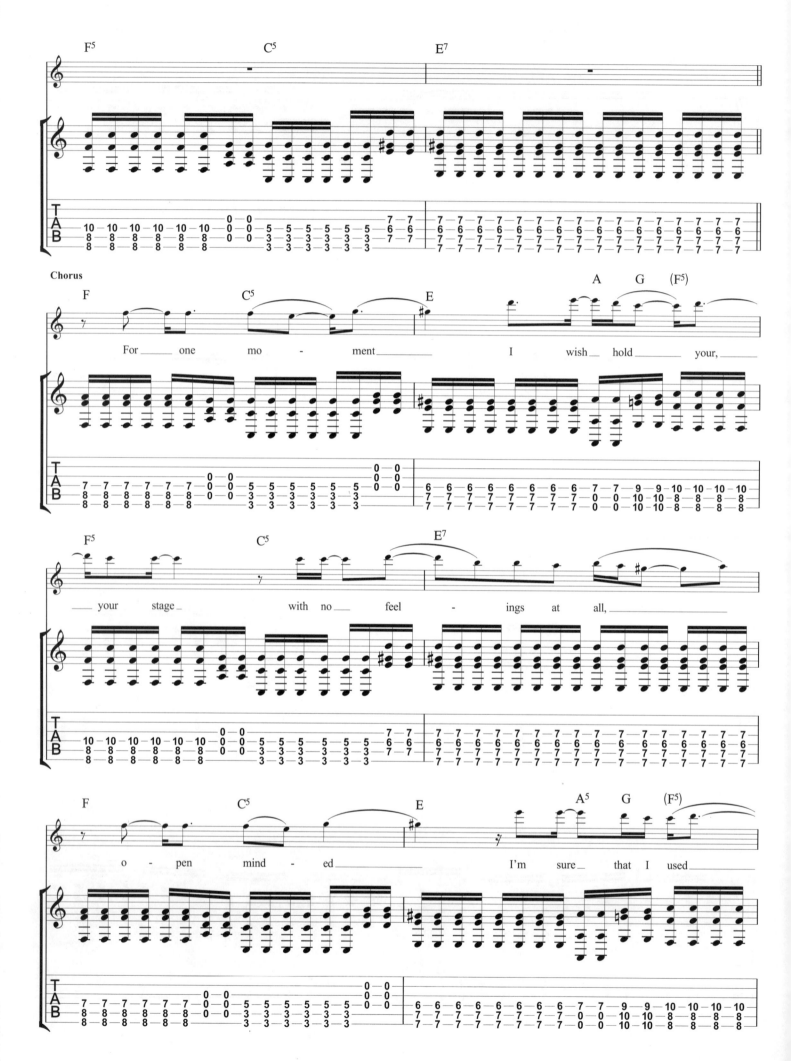

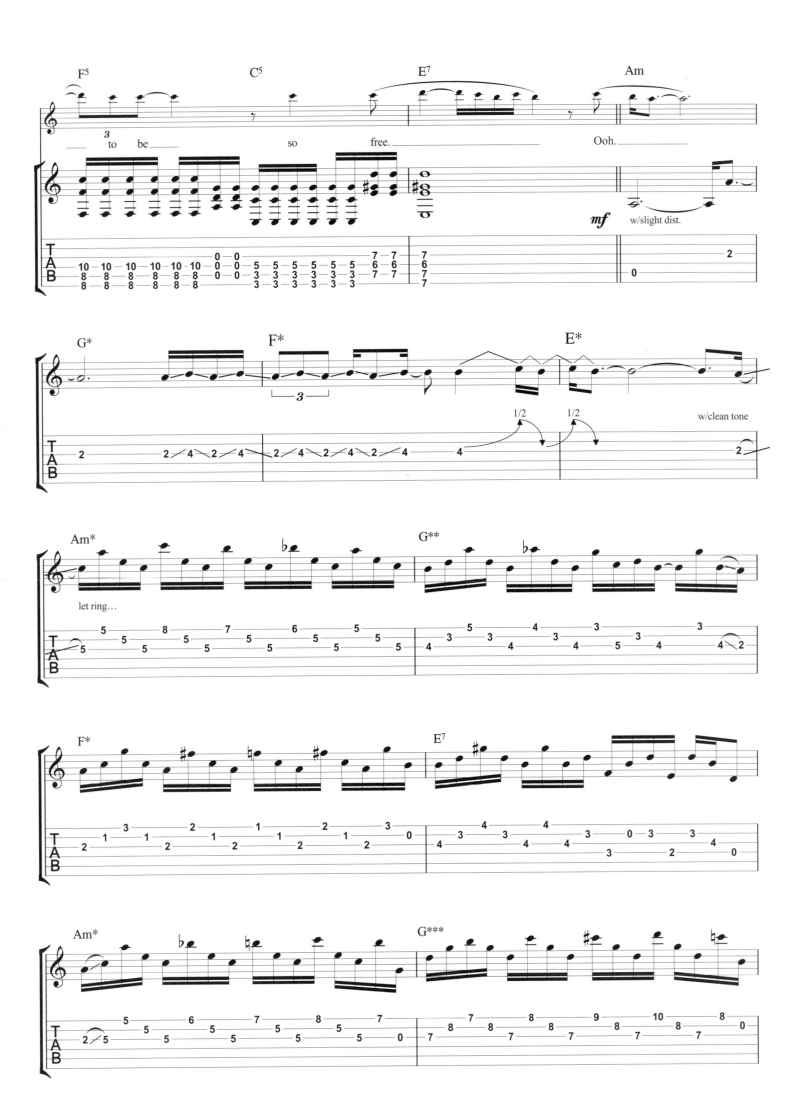

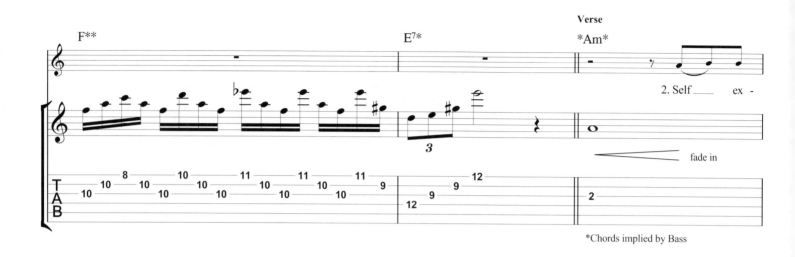

*Chords implied by Bass

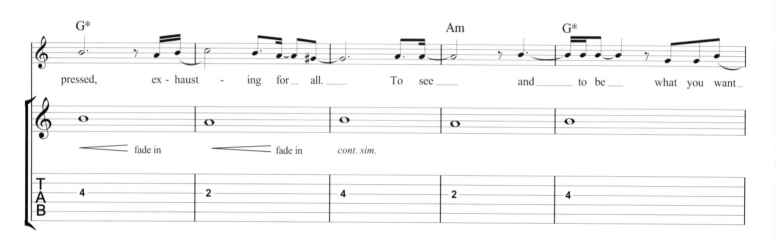

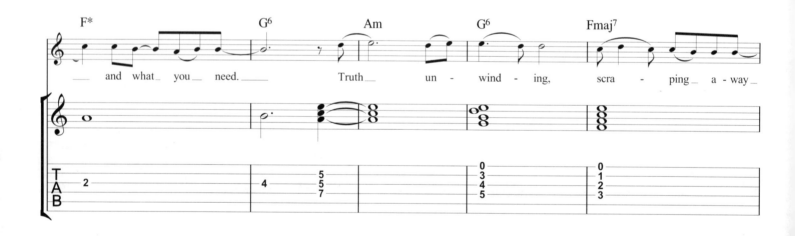

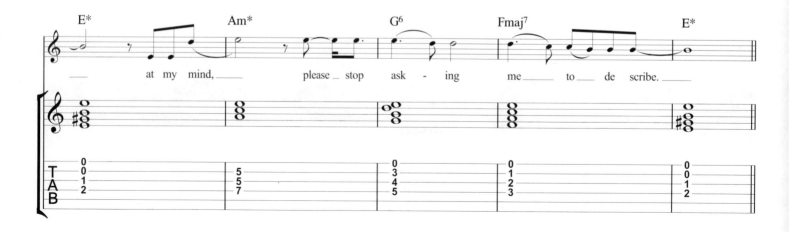

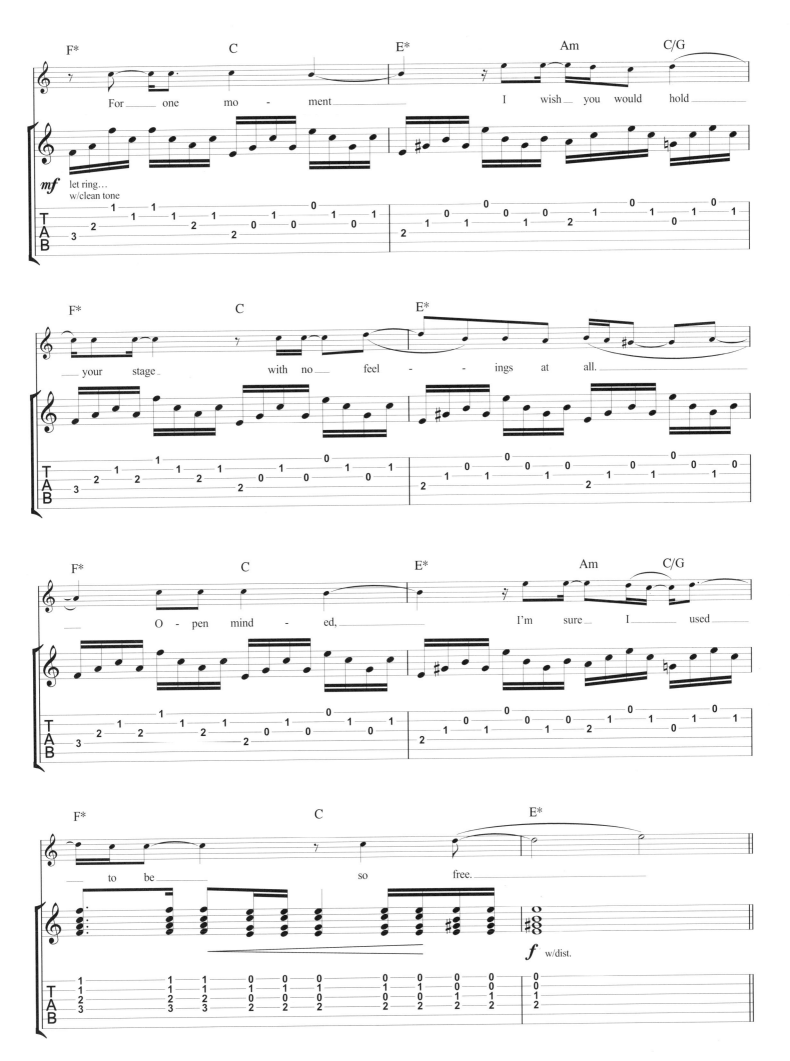

*Play open harmonic between 2nd & 3rd frets

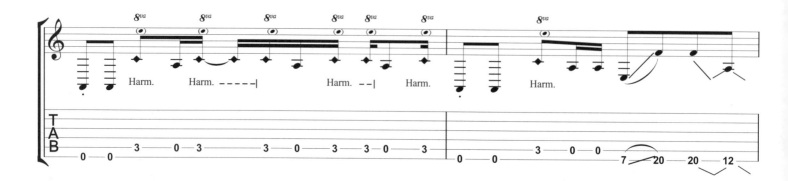

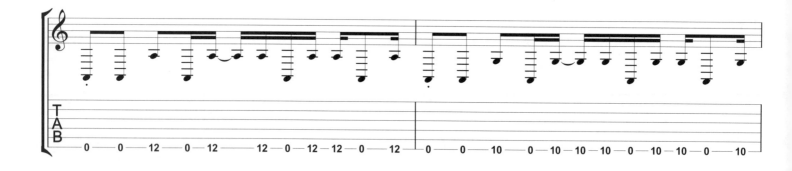

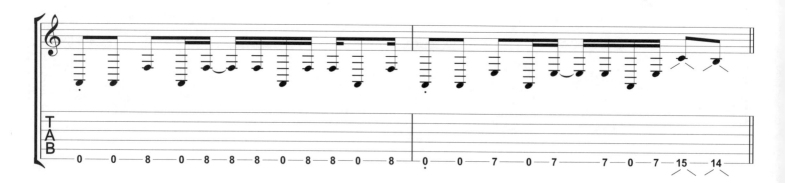

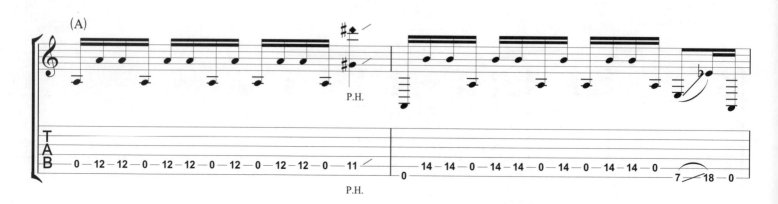

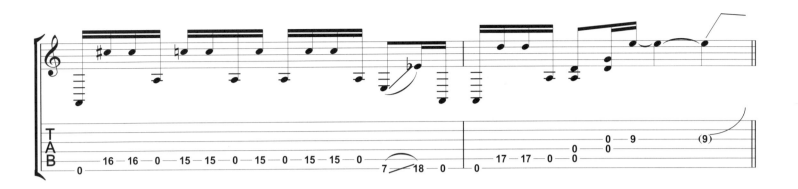

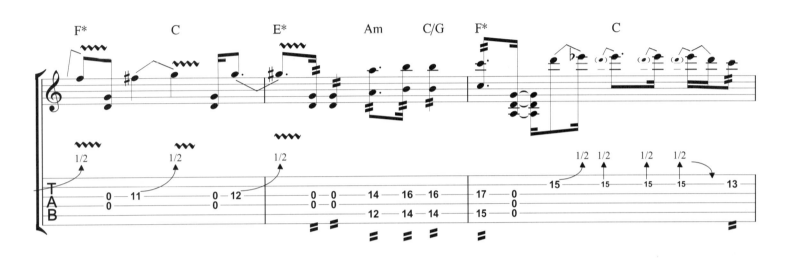

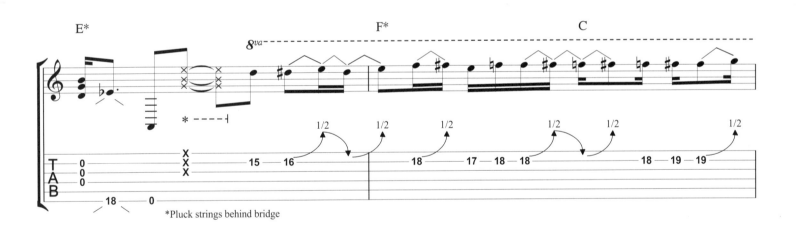

*Pluck strings behind bridge

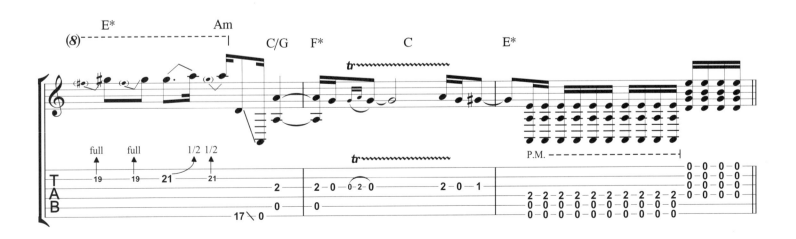

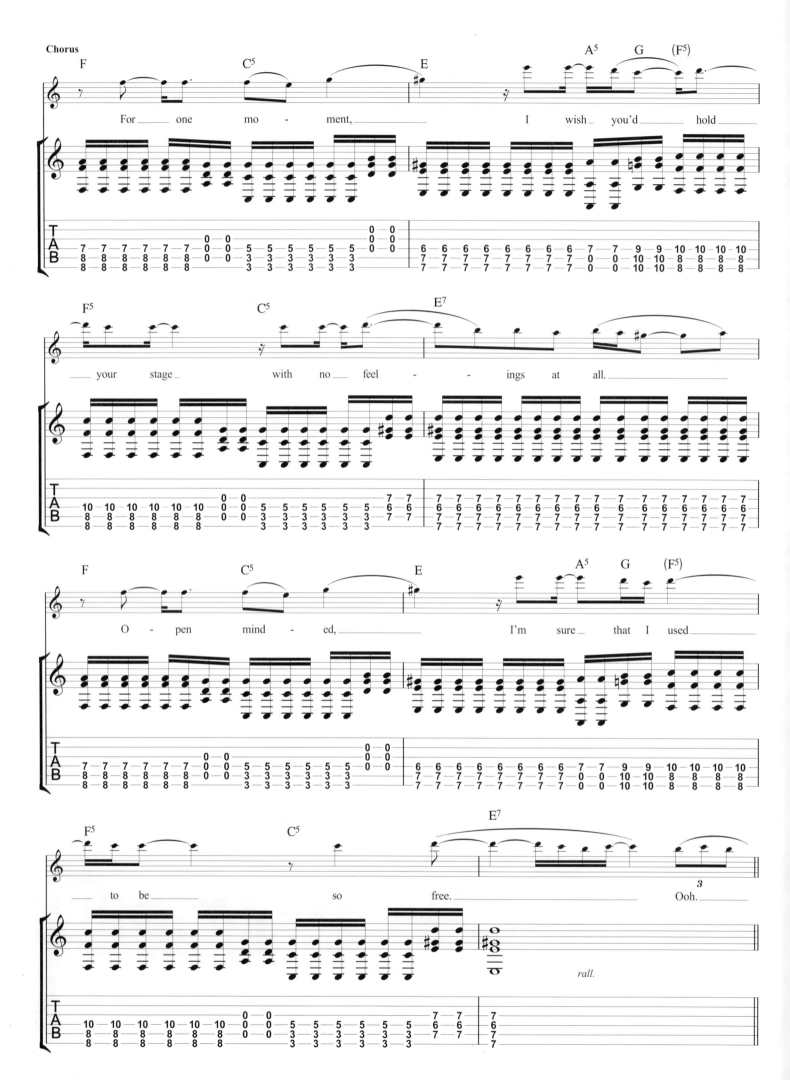

Chorus

90

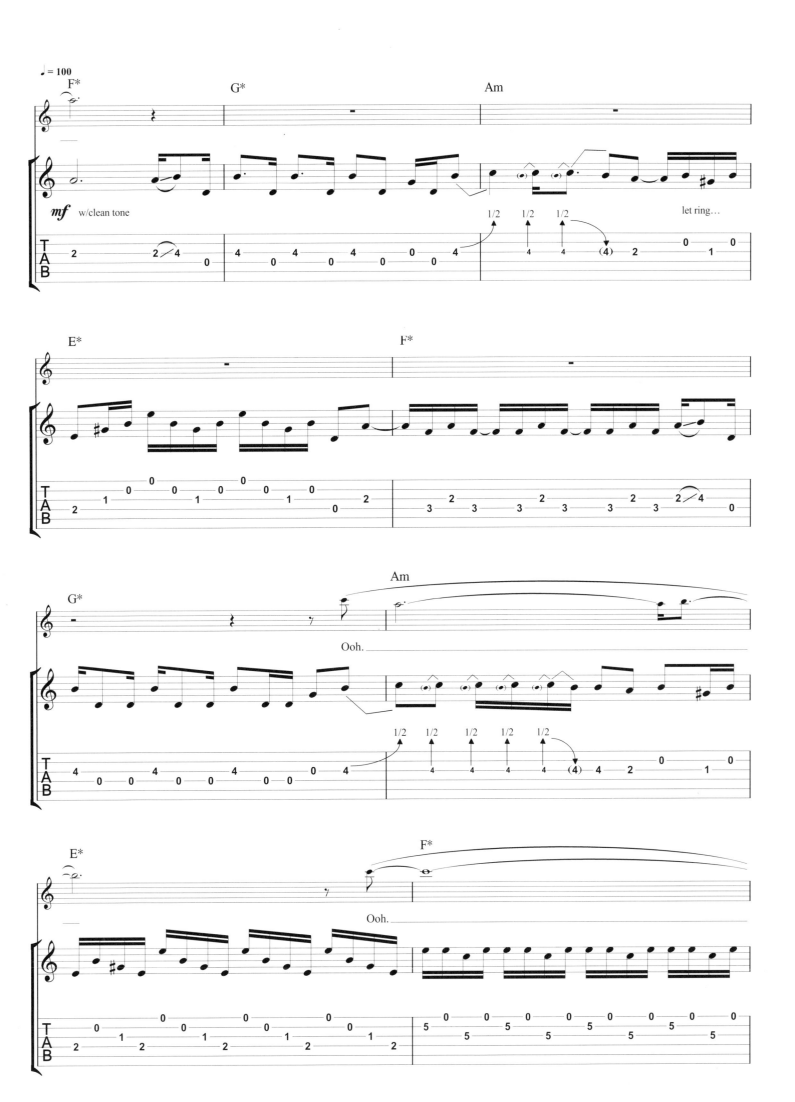

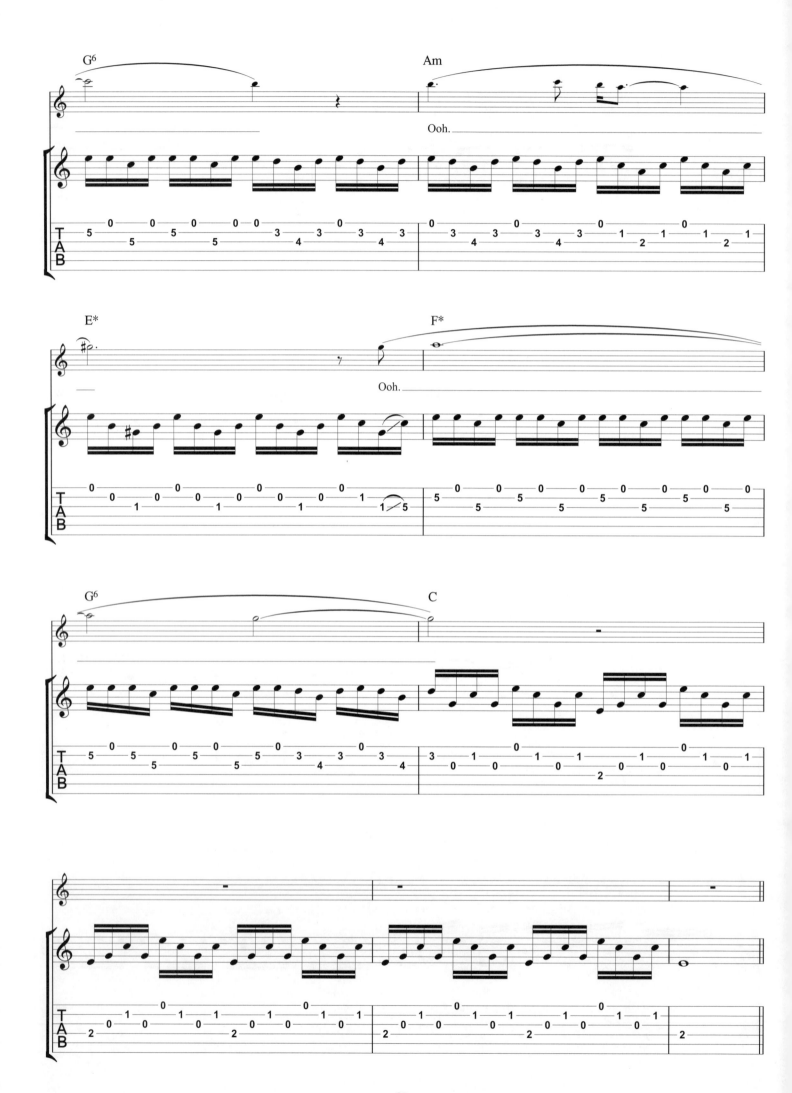

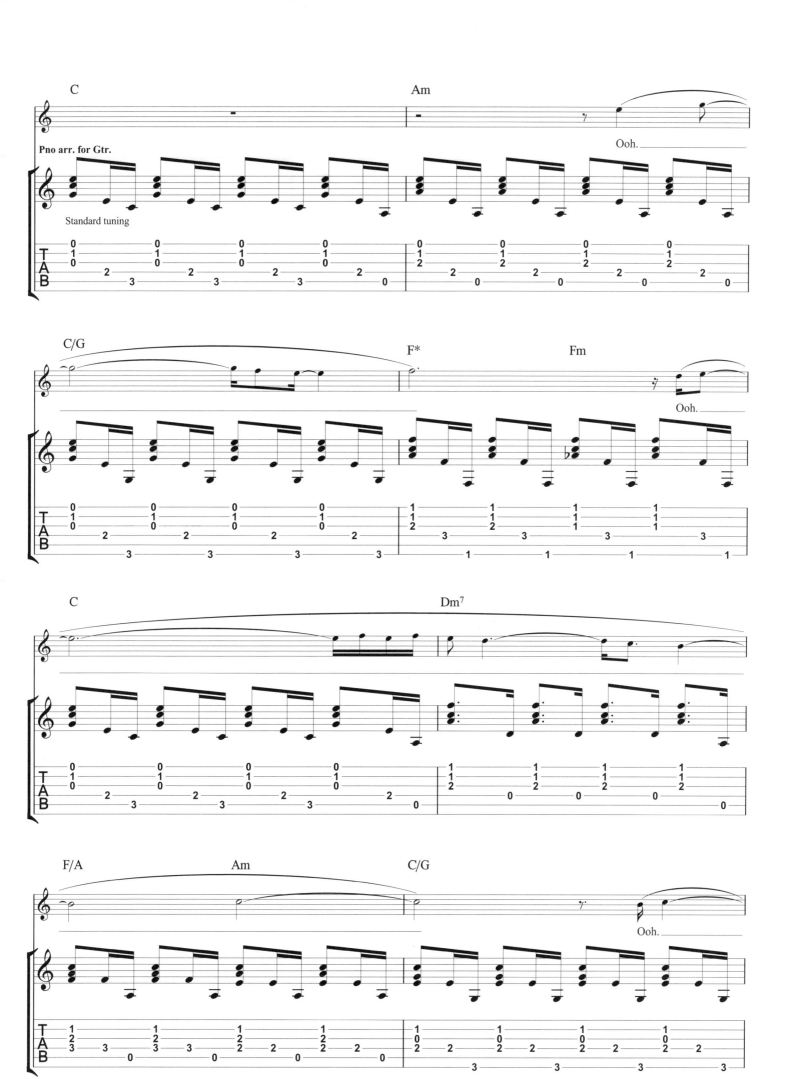

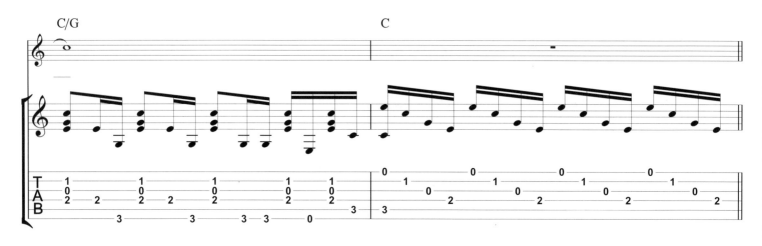

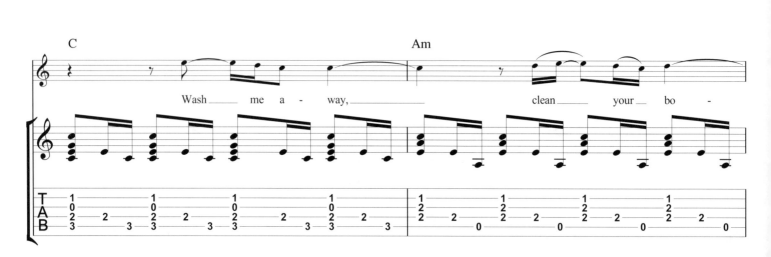

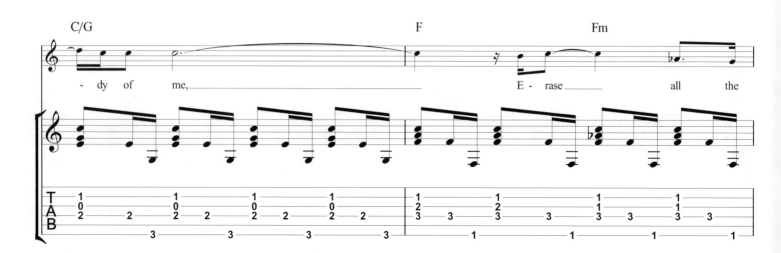

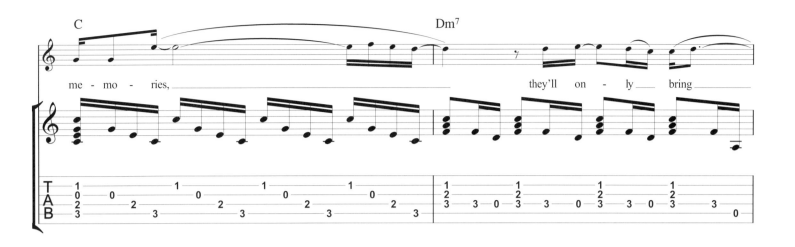

me - mo - ries, _____ they'll on - ly bring

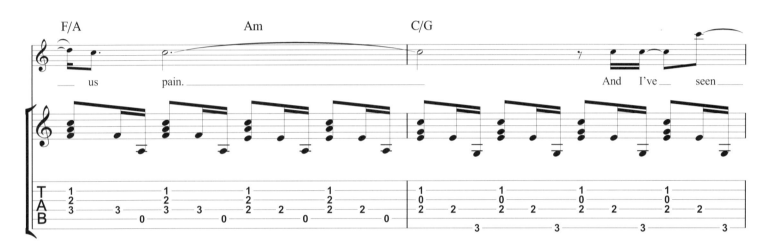

___ us pain. _____ And I've seen

all _____ I _____ need.

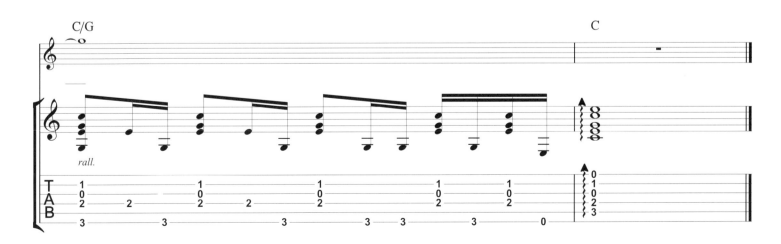

SHOWBIZ

Lyrics & Music by Matthew Bellamy

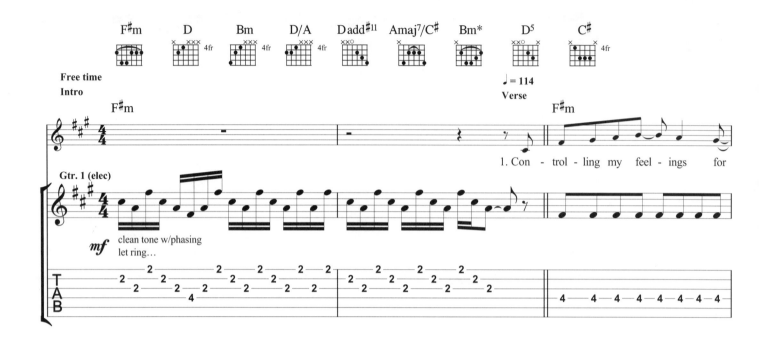

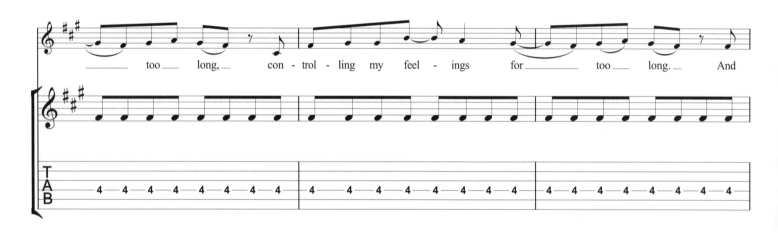

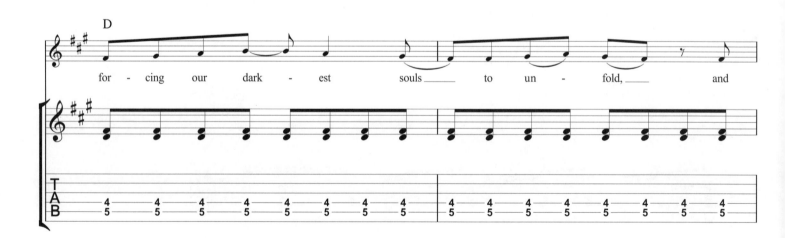

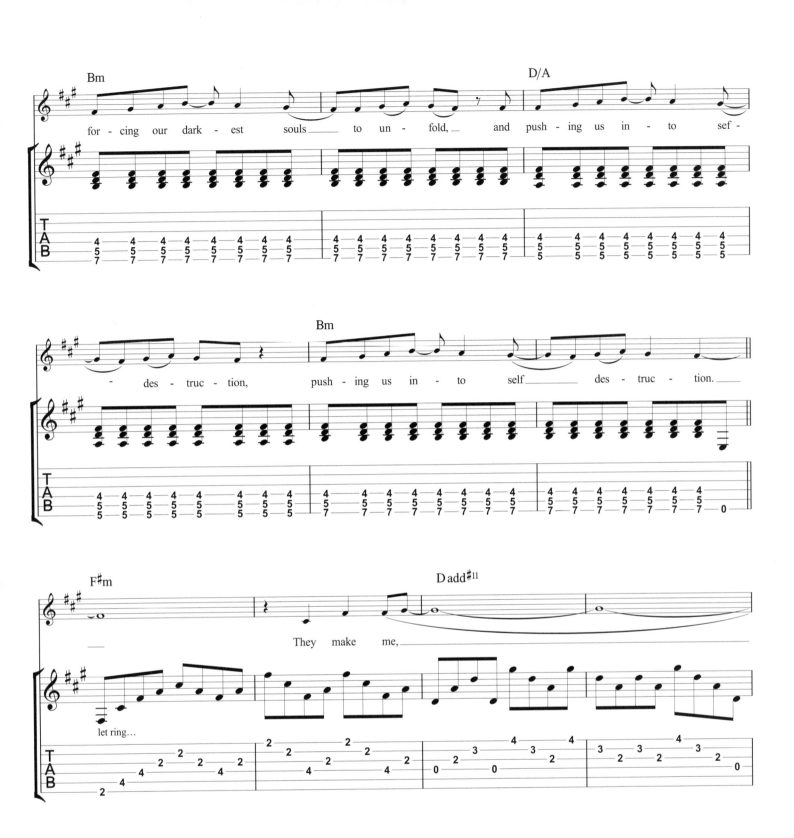

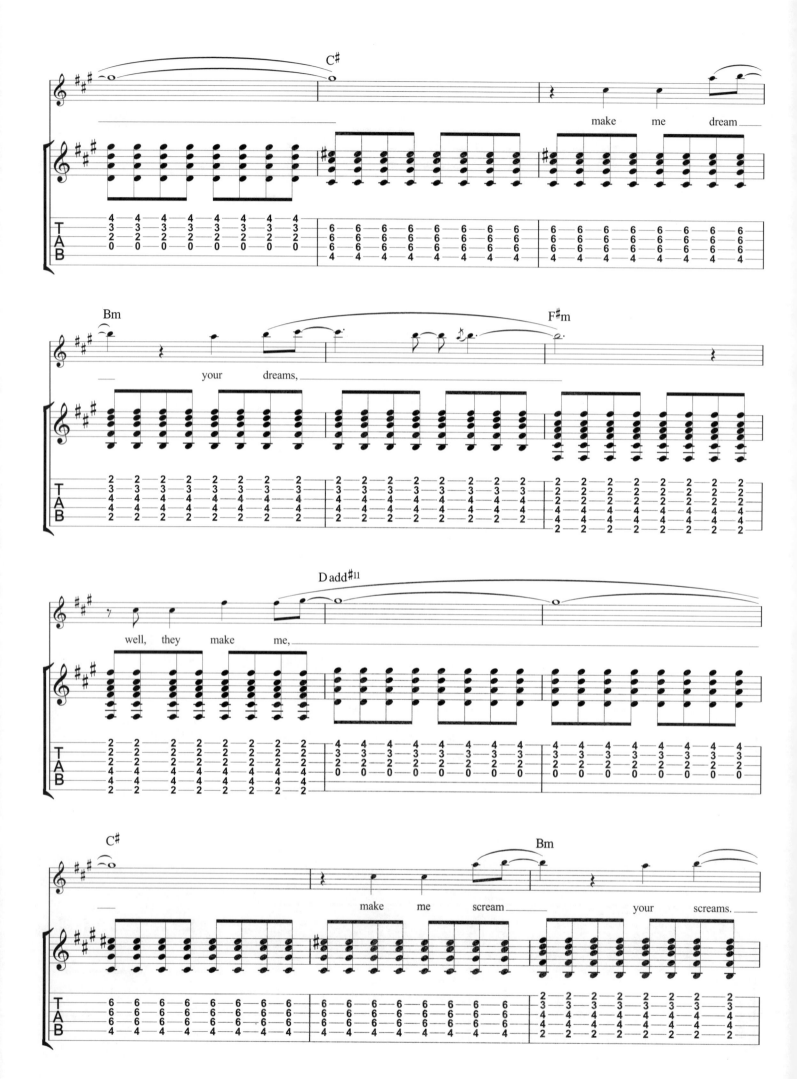

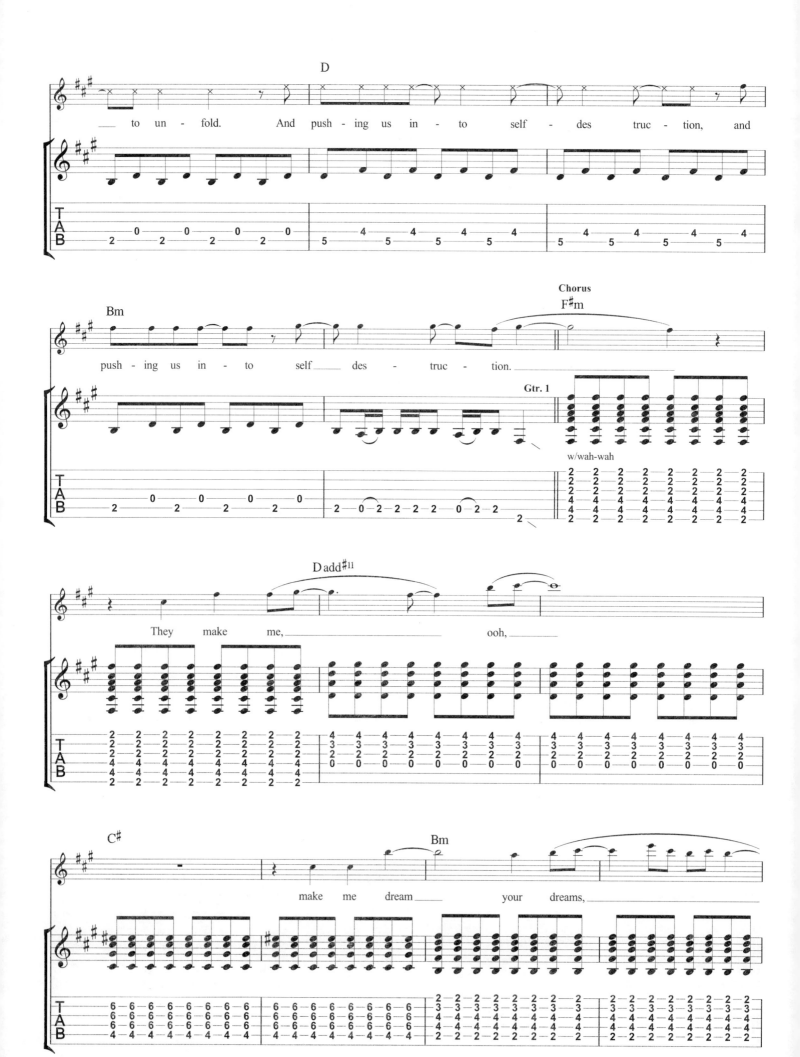

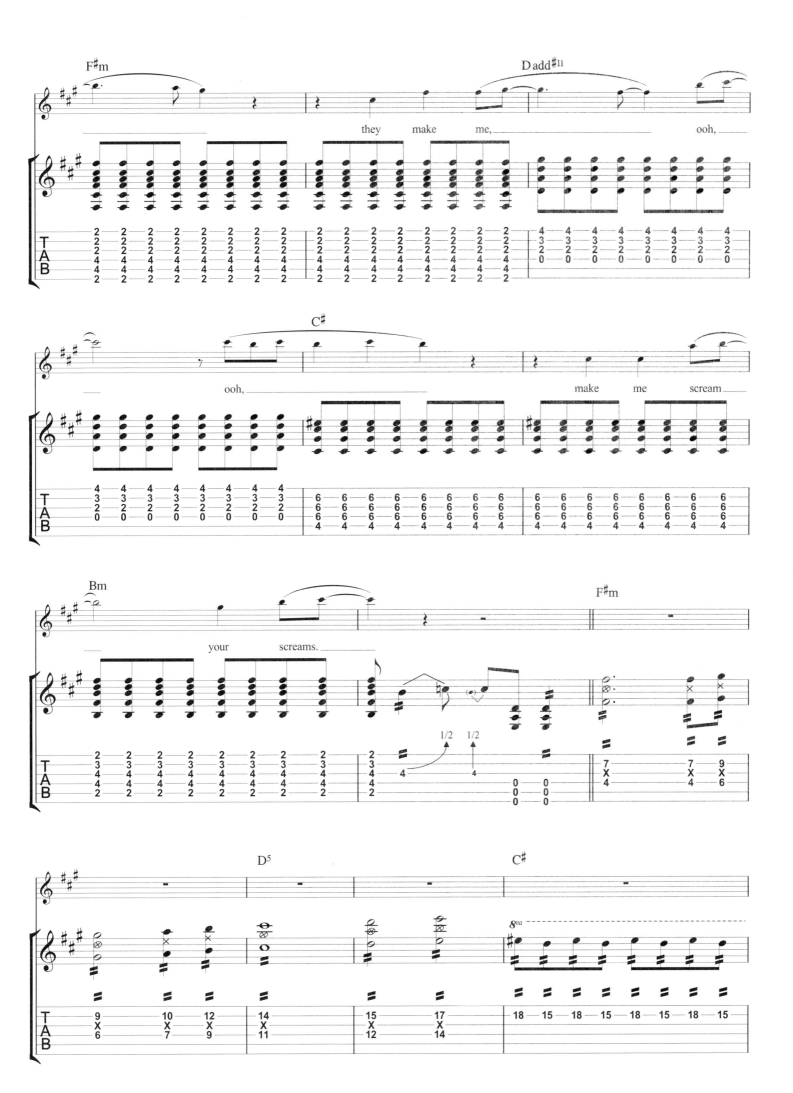

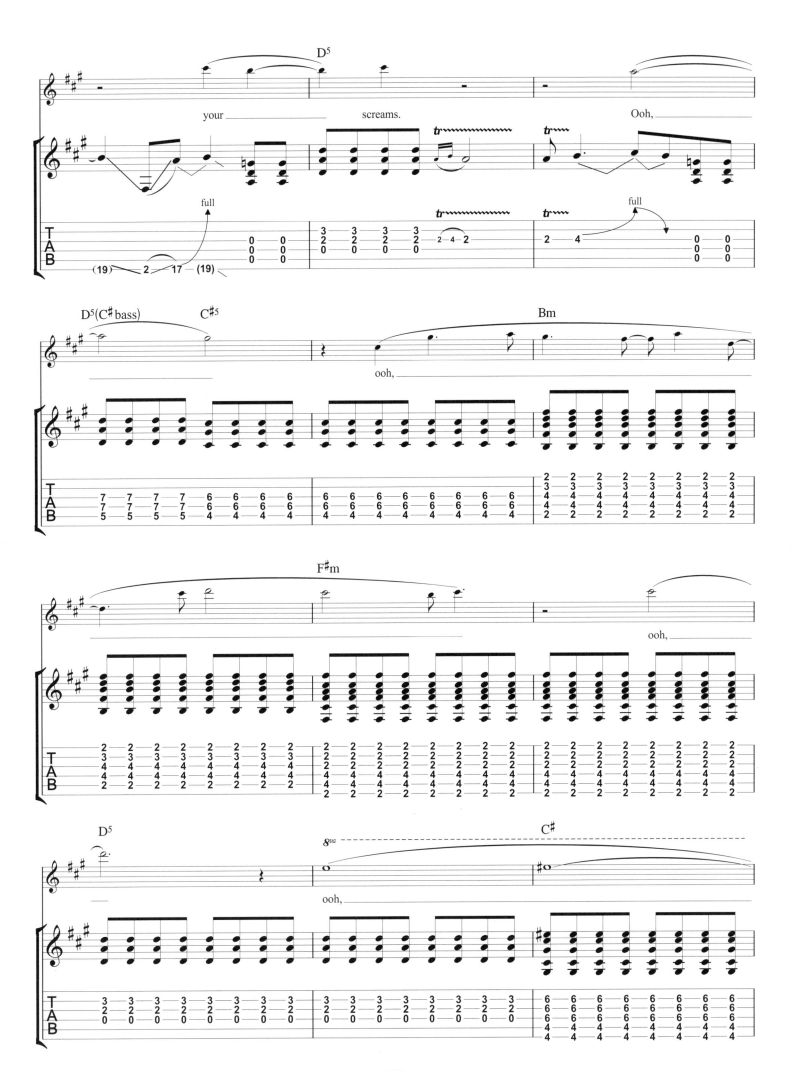

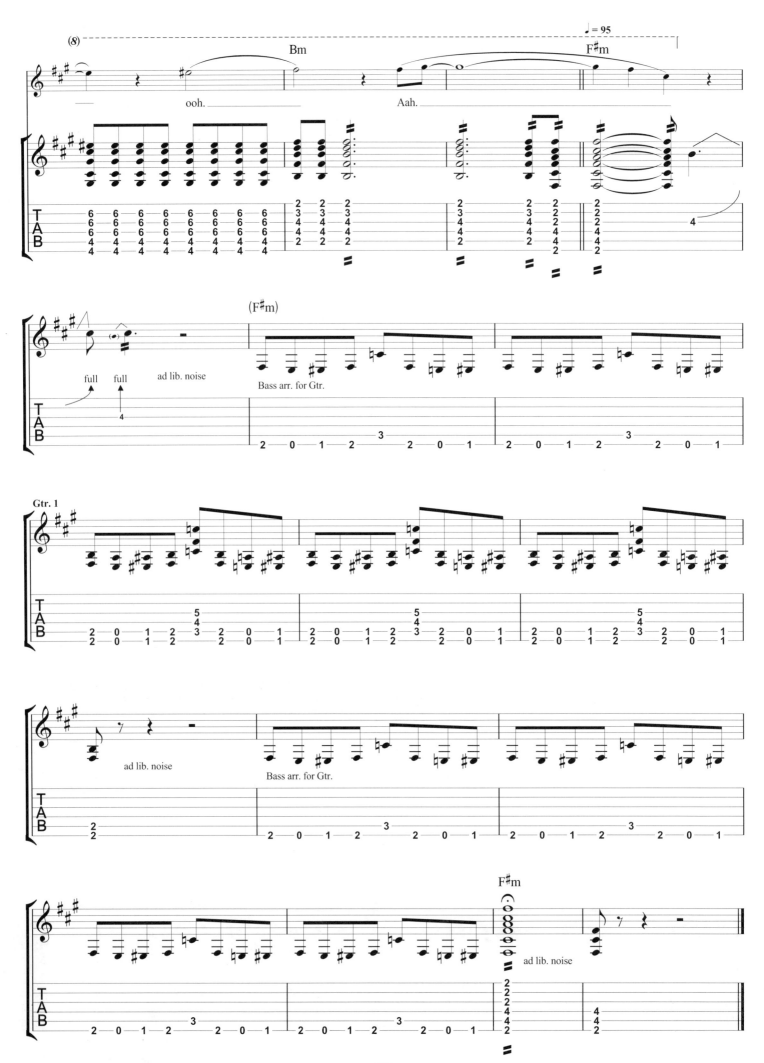

MEGALOMANIA

Lyrics & Music by Matthew Bellamy

Em

Gtr (acous.)

cont. *sim.*

Ooh. Ooh.

Strings

Bass

1° bass cont. sim.

Organ (2° only)

1° strings
w/Fig. 1

1. Par - a - dise comes at a
2. Use - less de - vice, it won't suf -

F#m¹¹   Am   B⁷

price that I am not pre - pared to pay.
fice, I want a new game to play.

8vb

Em   Am/C   G/B   Am

What are we here for?
When I am gone, it won't be

108

Could some - one tell me please.

long be - fore I dis - turb you in the dark.

The good news is she can't have

And par - a - dise comes at a

ba - bies, and won't ac - cept gifts from me.

price that I am not pre - pared to pay.

What are they for? They'll just

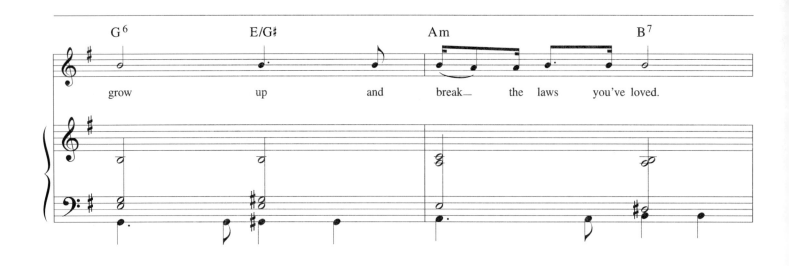

grow up and break— the laws you've loved.

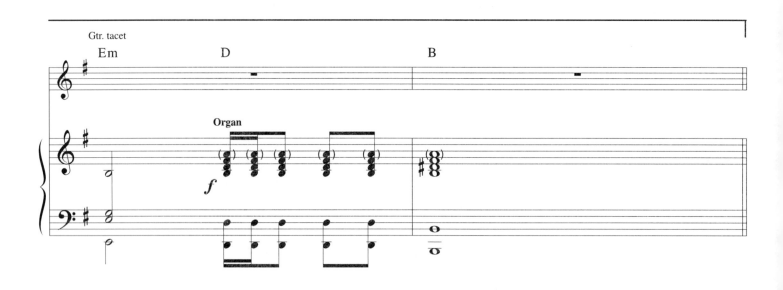

What were— we— built— for?—

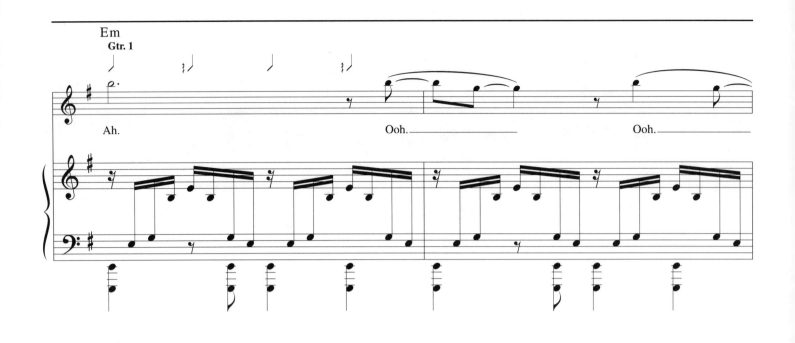

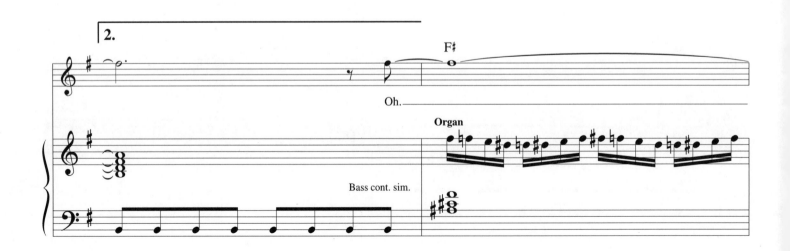

DARK SHINES

Lyrics & Music by Matthew Bellamy

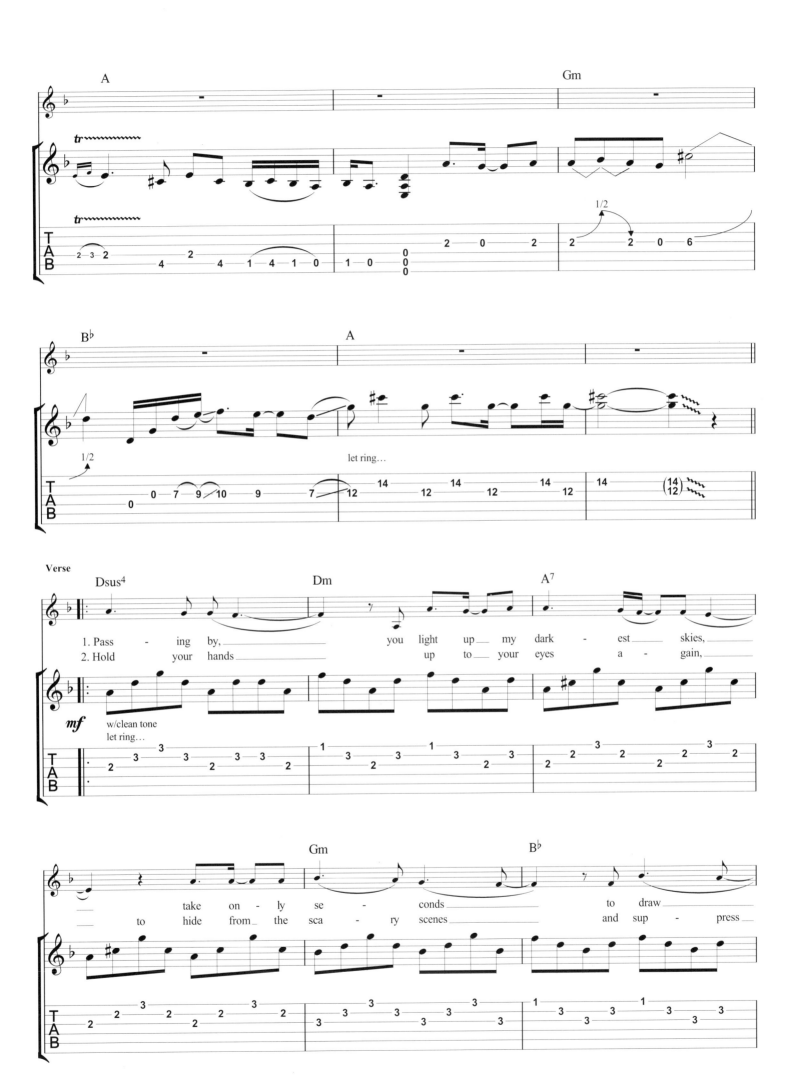

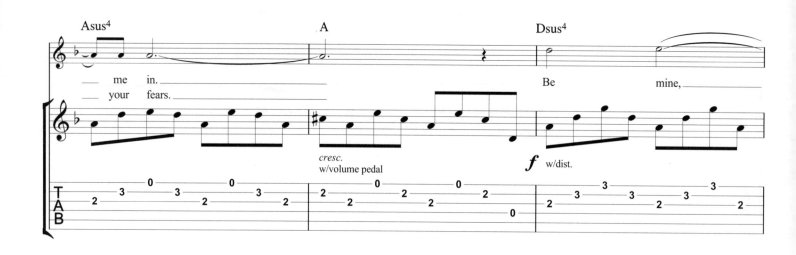

me in. / your fears.

Be mine,

and your in-

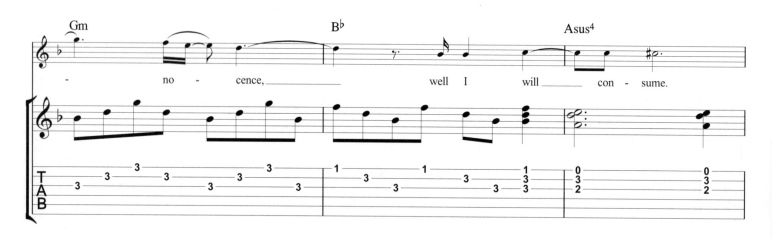

-no - cence, well I will con - sume.

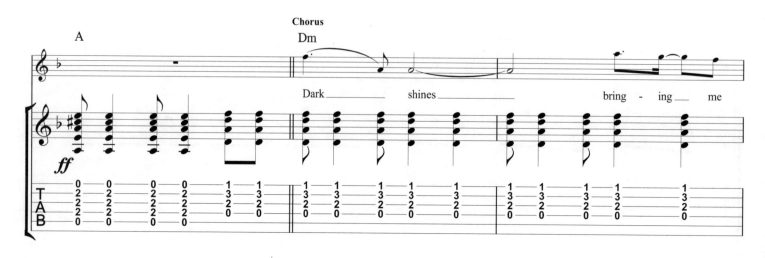

Dark shines bring - ing me

116

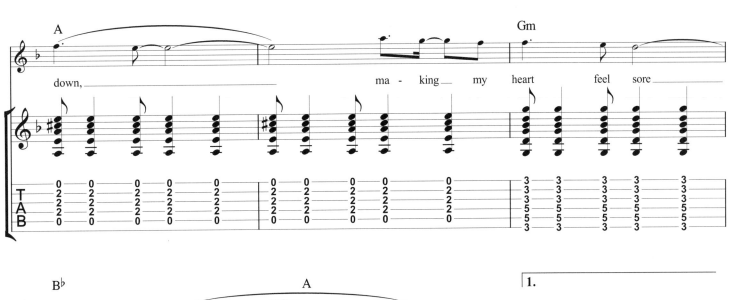

down,_____   ma - king__ my heart   feel sore_____

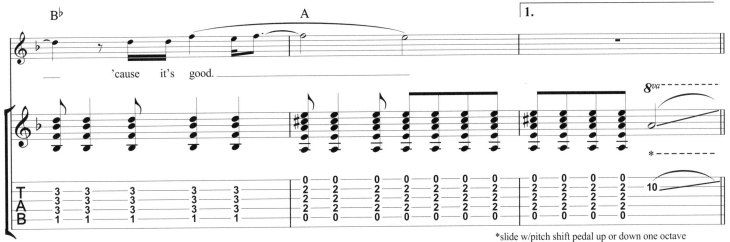

'cause   it's   good._____

*slide w/pitch shift pedal up or down one octave

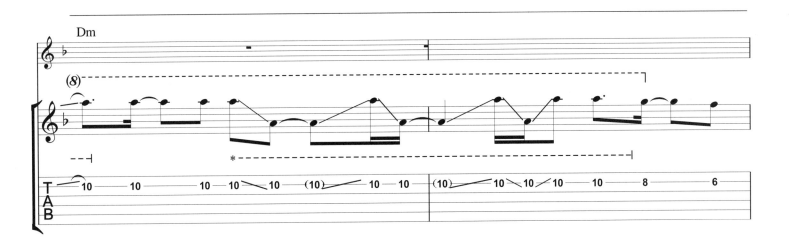

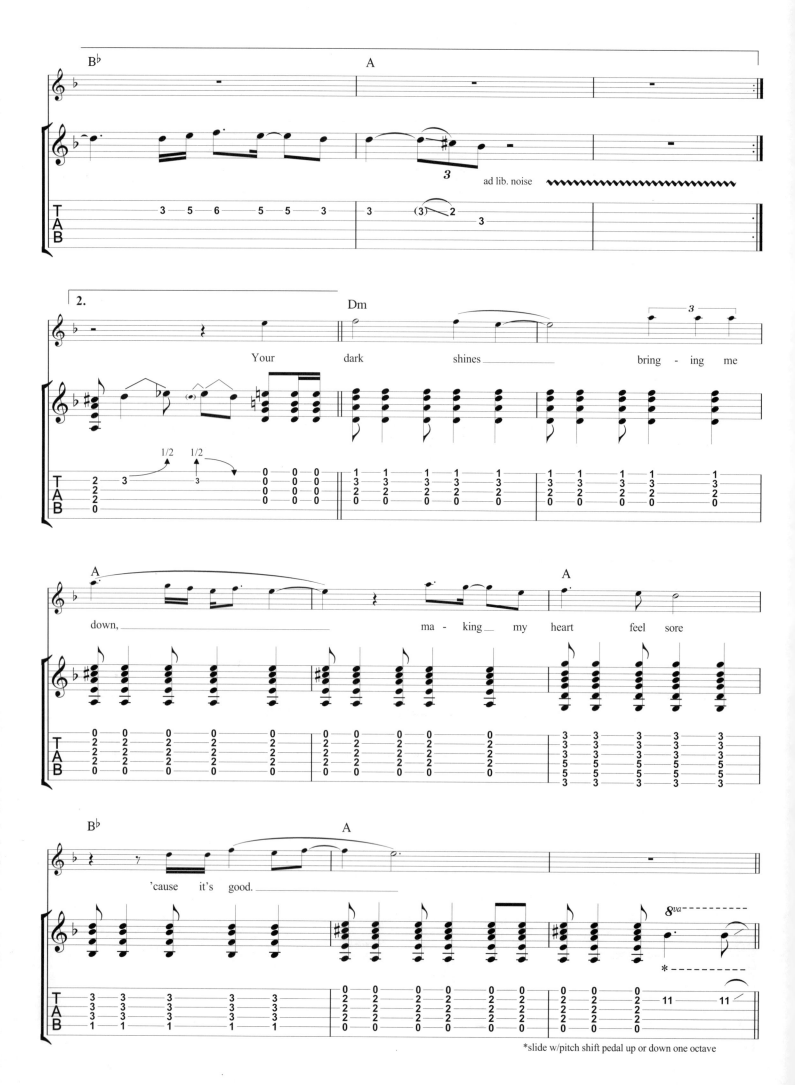

*slide w/pitch shift pedal up or down one octave

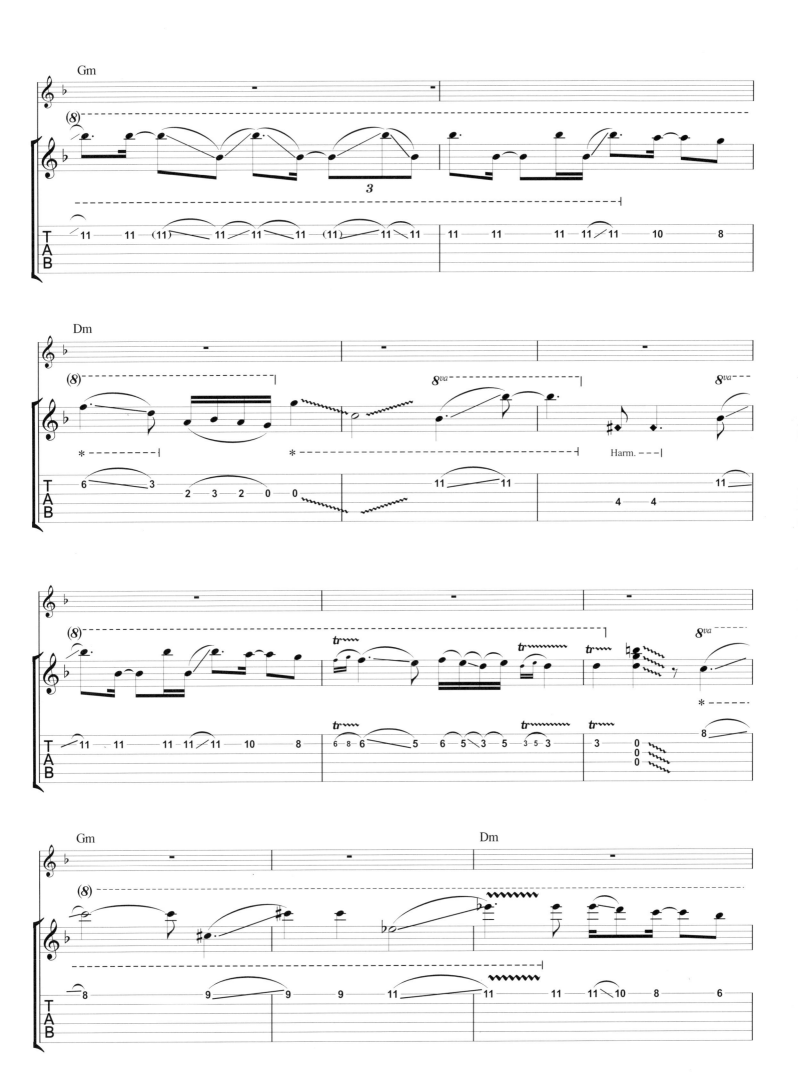

120

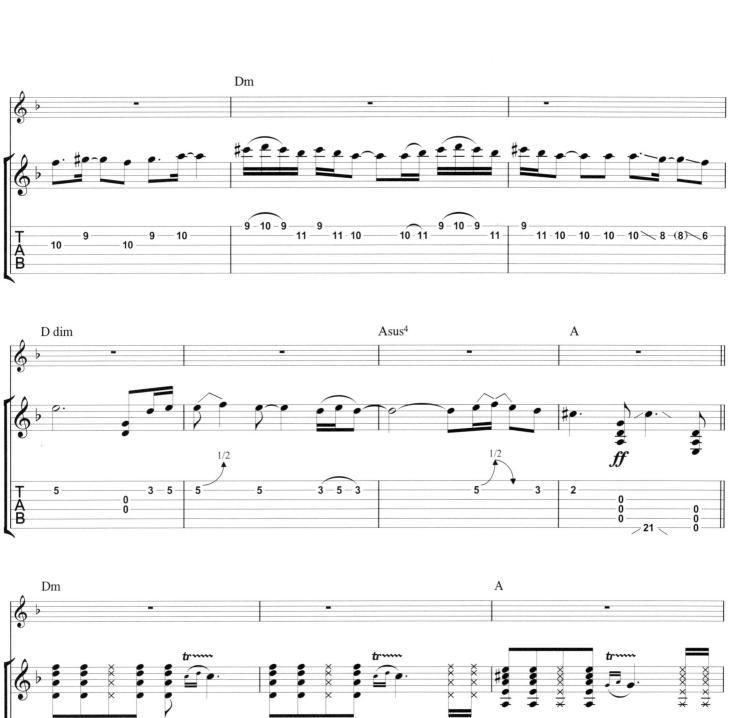

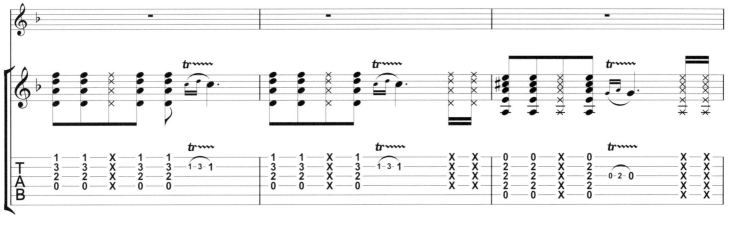

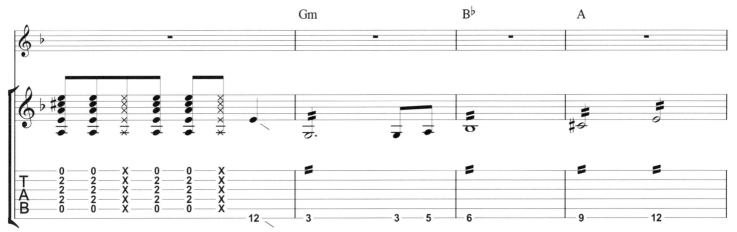

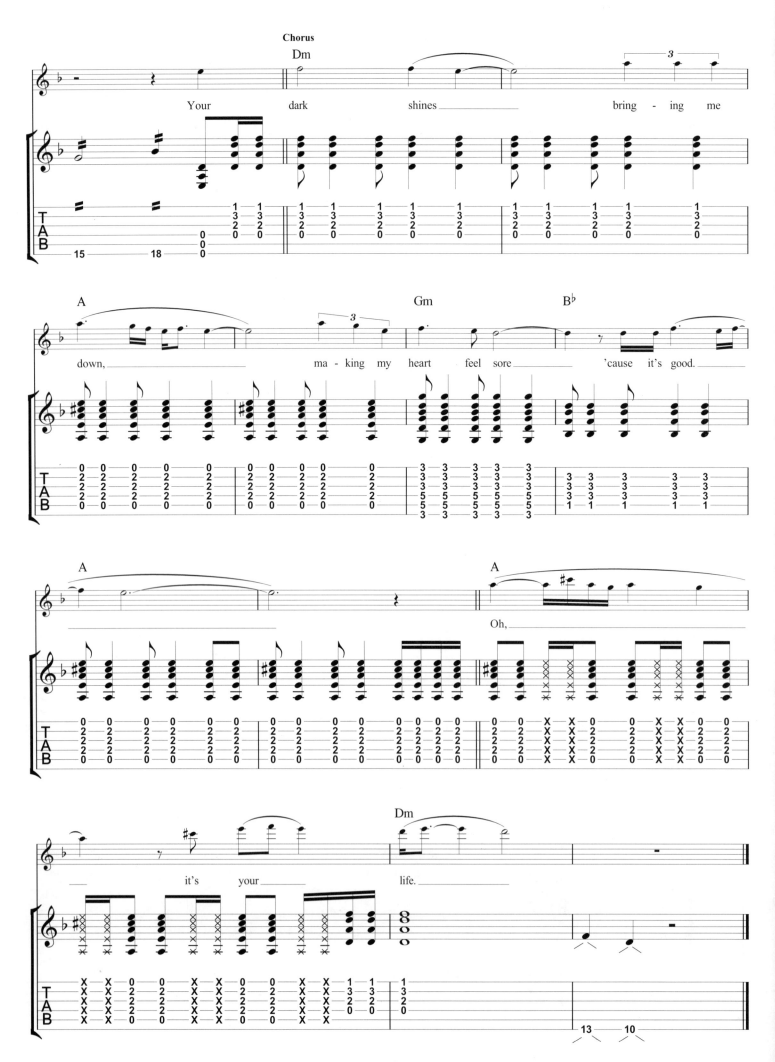

SCREENAGER

Lyrics & Music by Matthew Bellamy

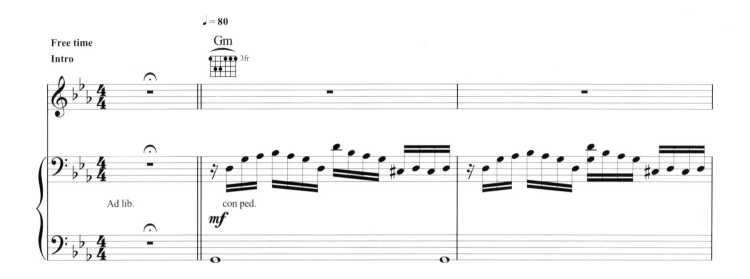

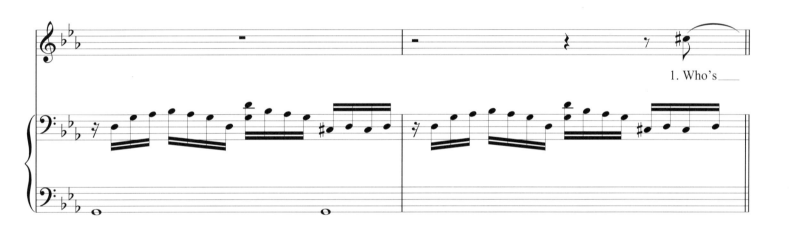

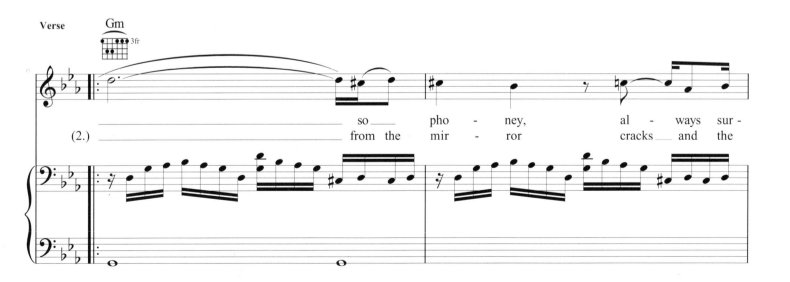

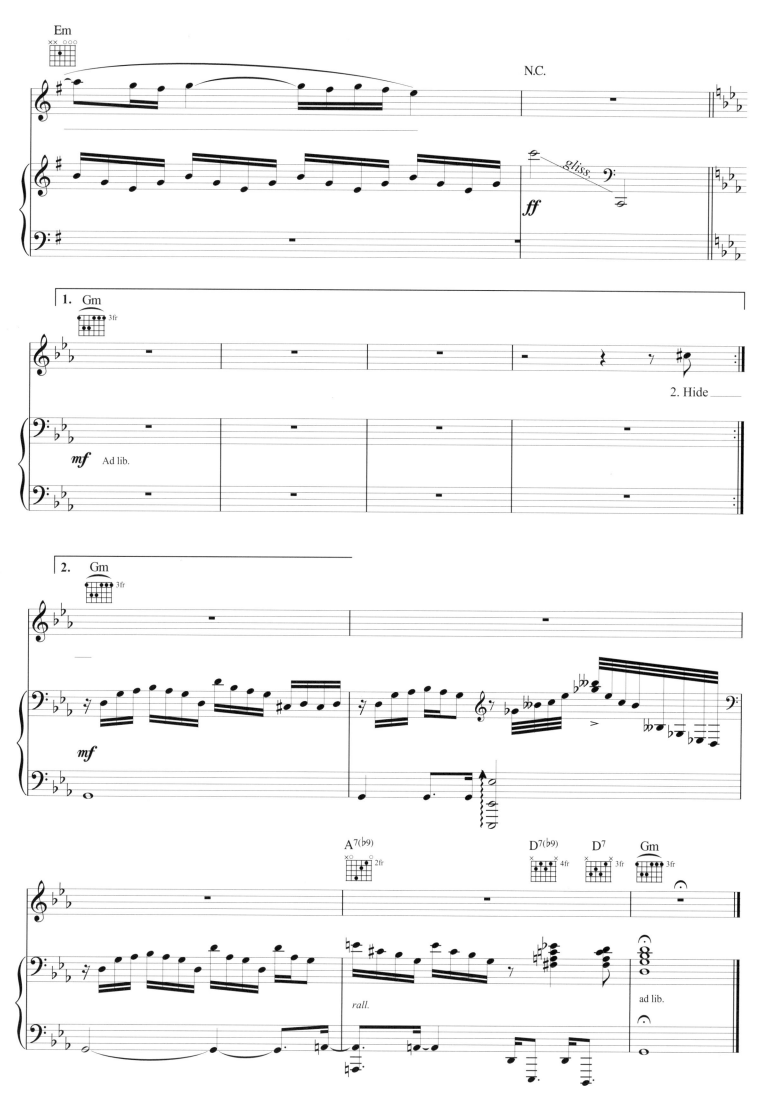

SPACE DEMENTIA

Lyrics & Music by Matthew Bellamy

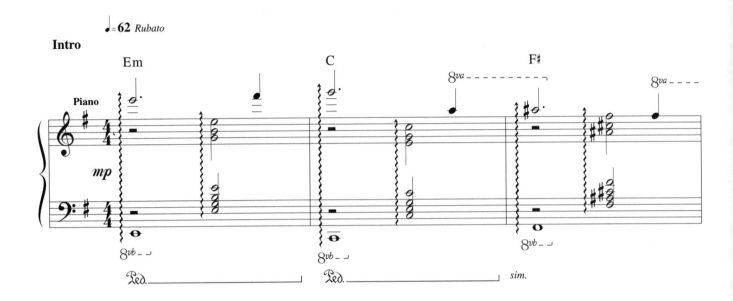

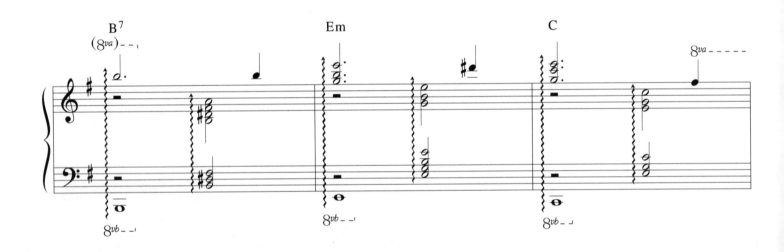

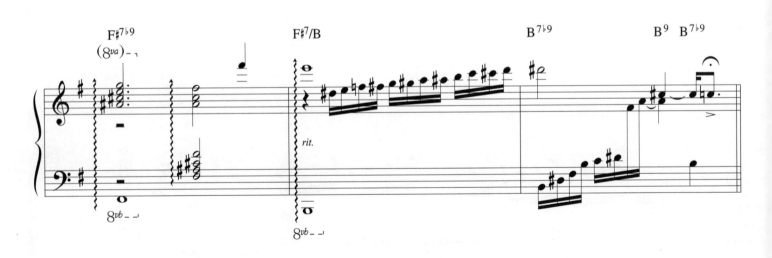

129

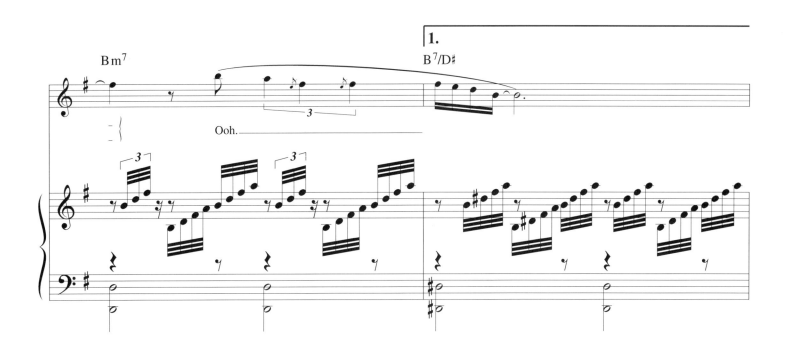

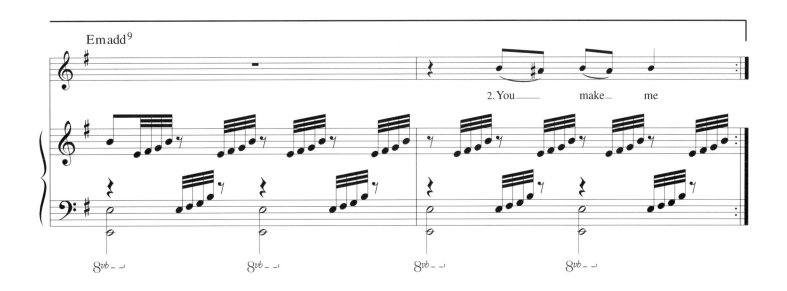

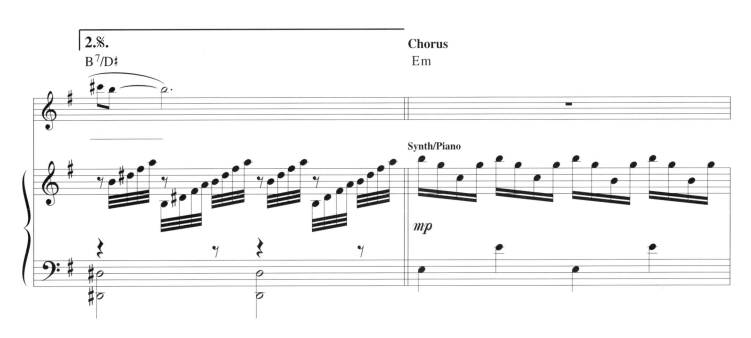

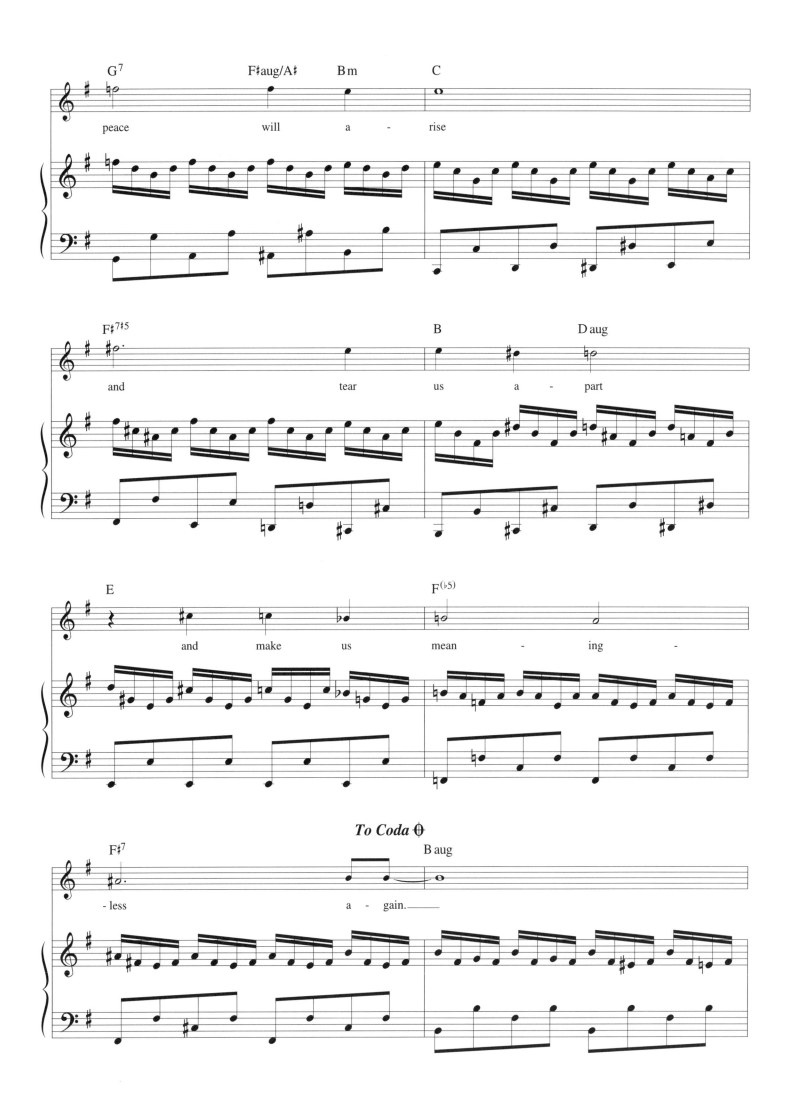

To Coda ⊕

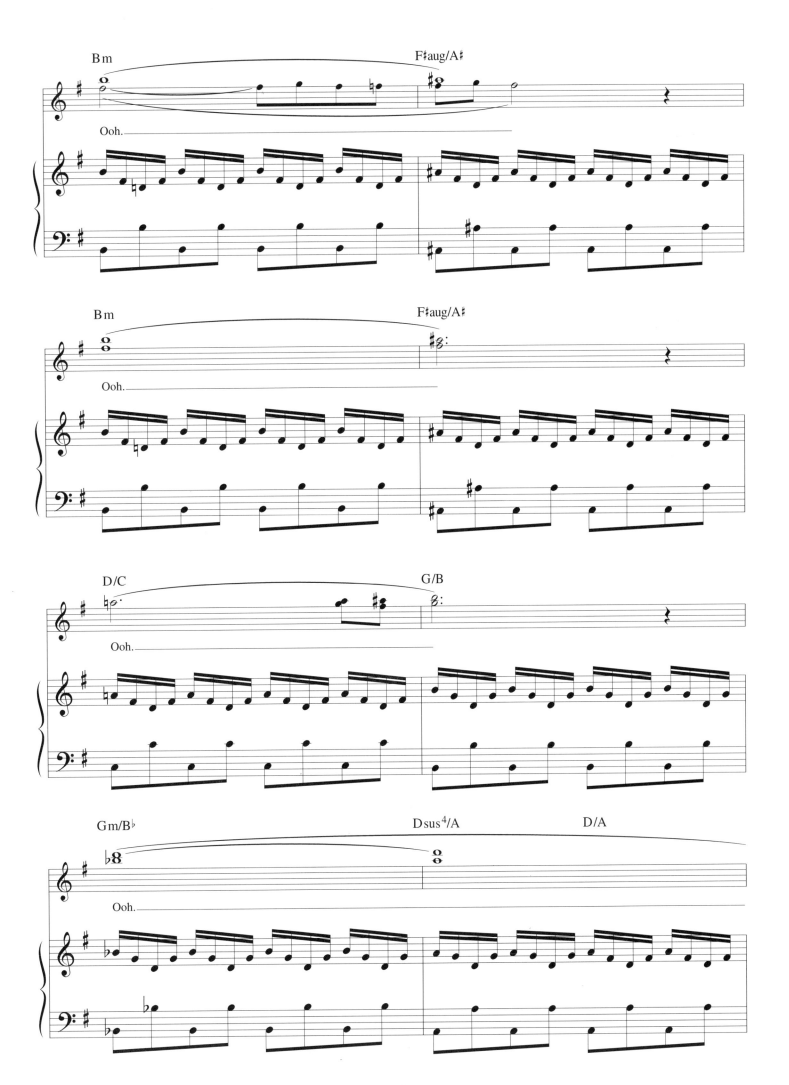

Verse 3:
You make us wanna die
I'd cut your name in my heart
We'll destroy this world for you
I know you want me to
Feel your pain.

IN YOUR WORLD

Lyrics & Music by Matthew Bellamy

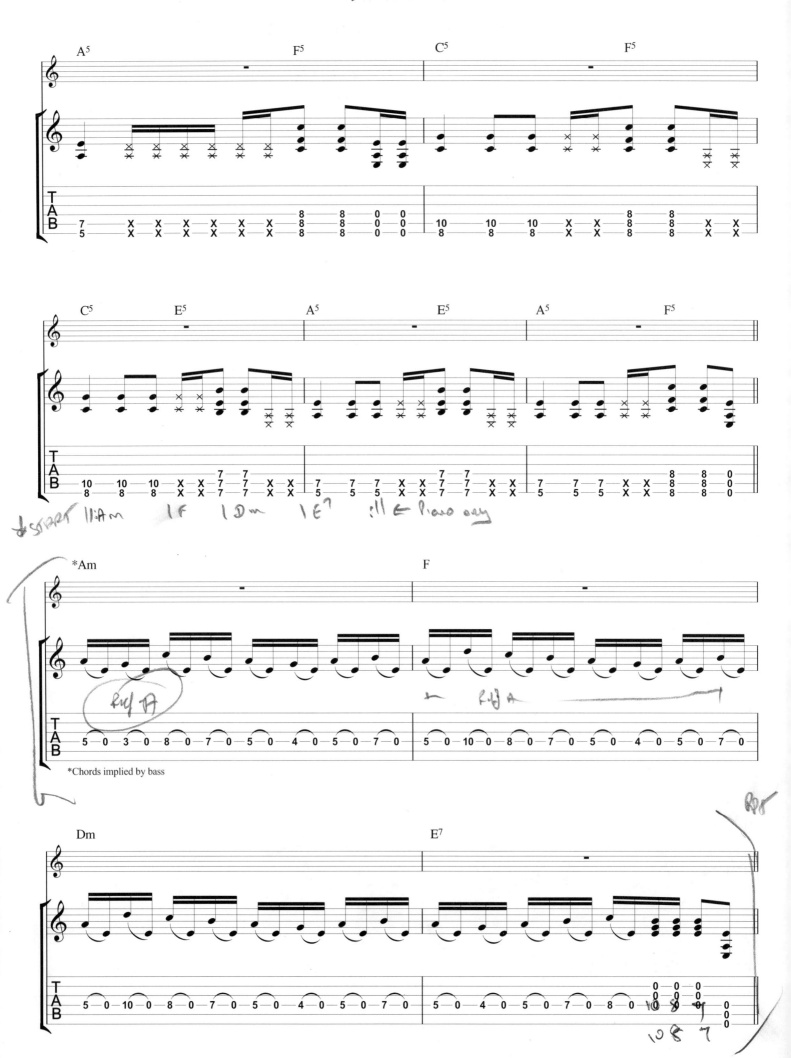

138

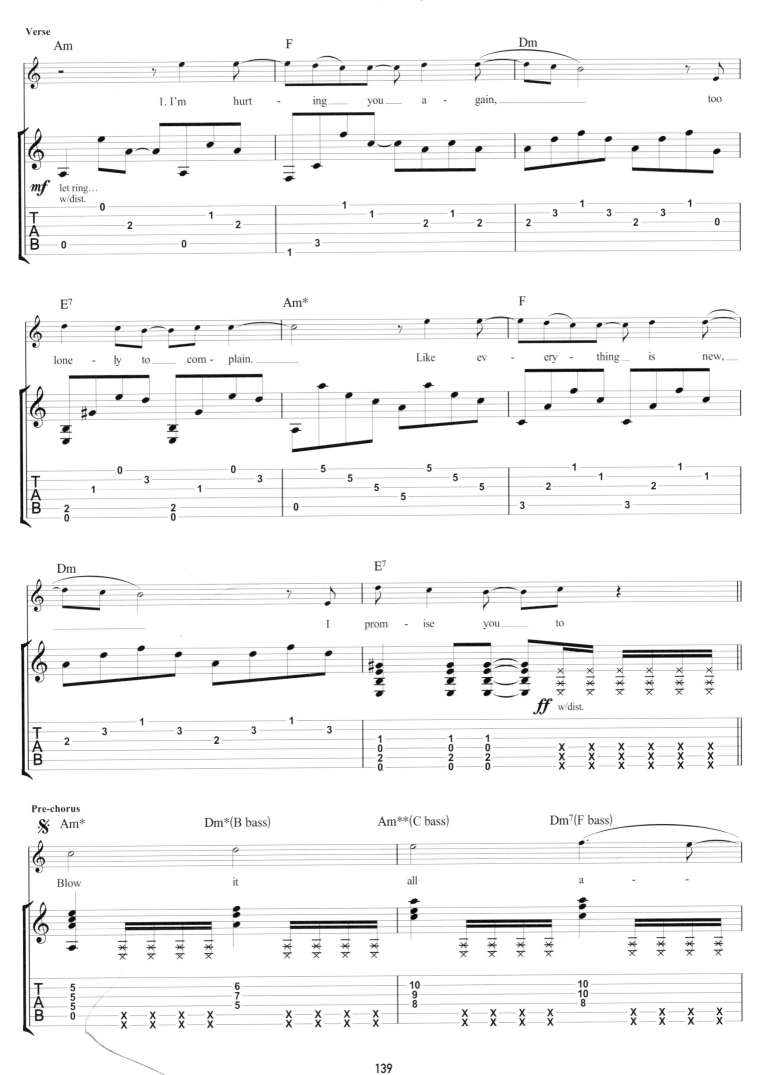

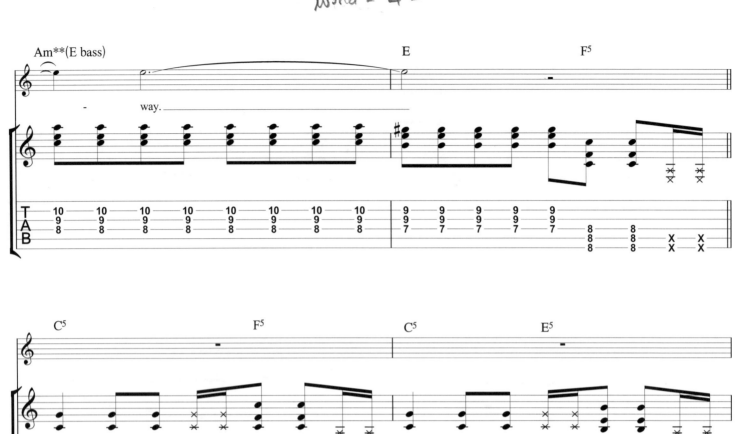

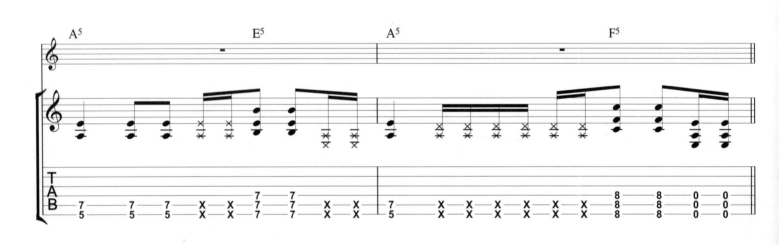

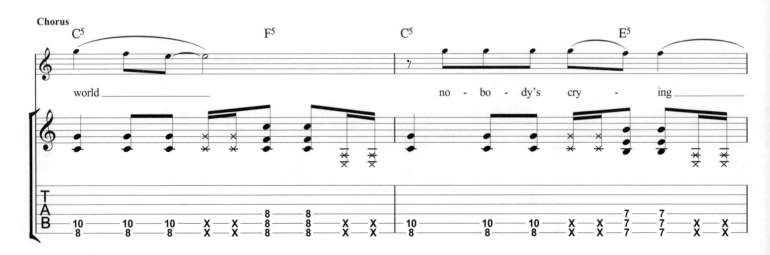

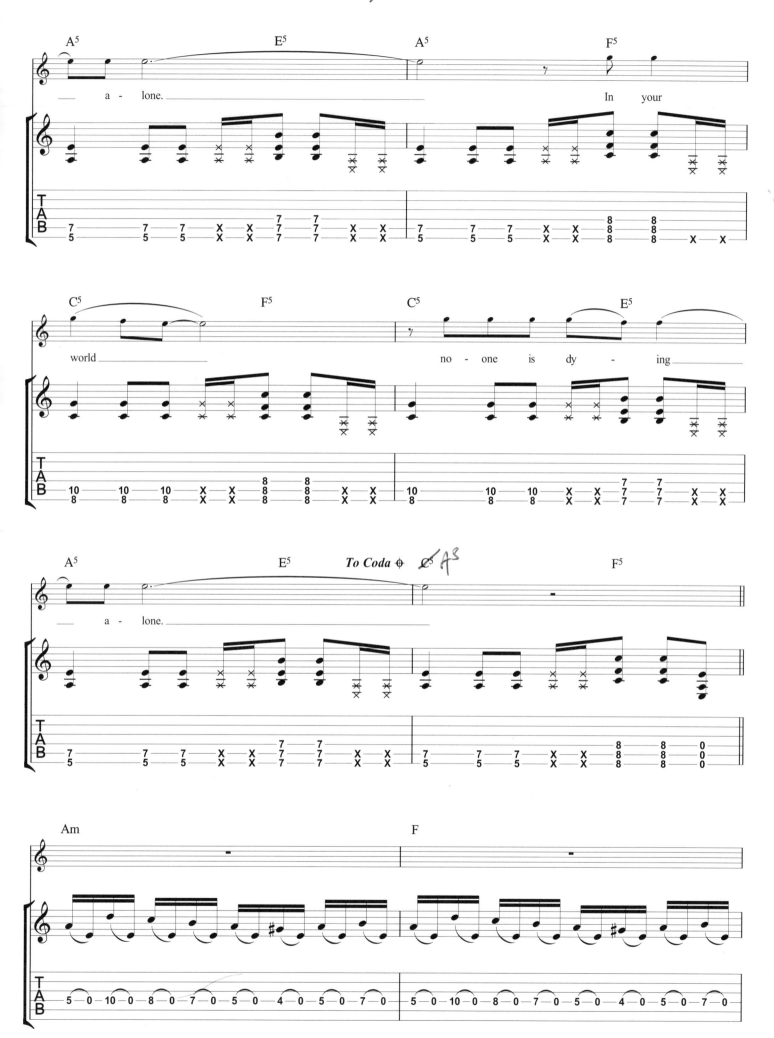

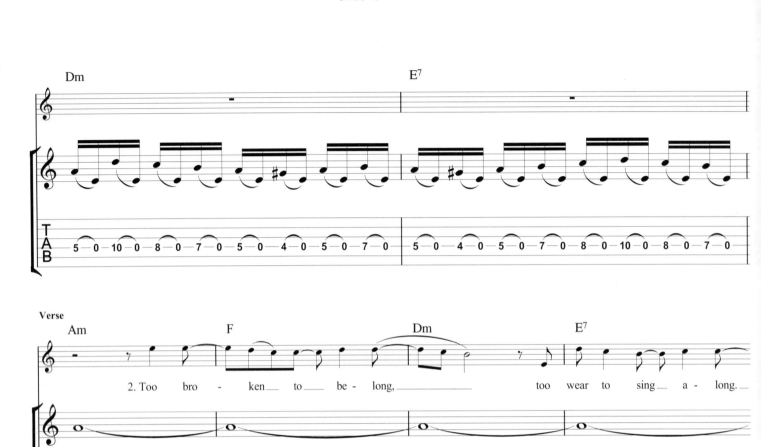

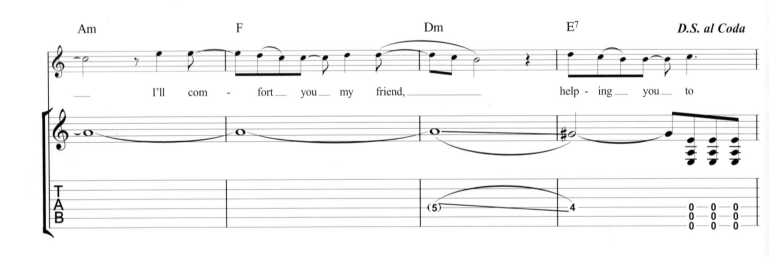

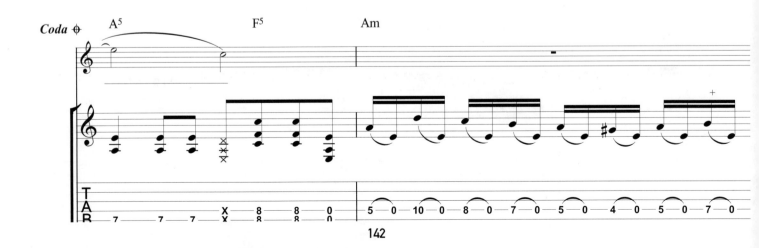

World - 7 -

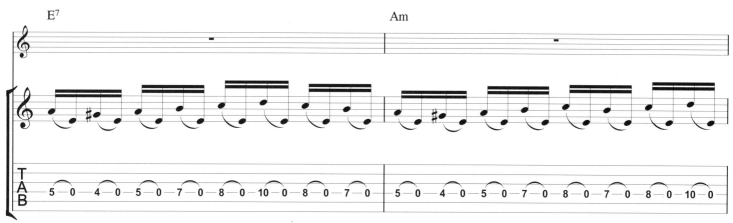

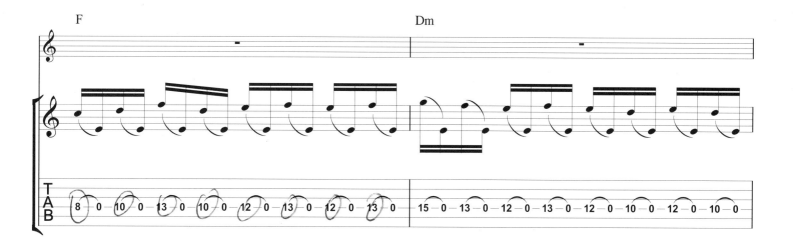

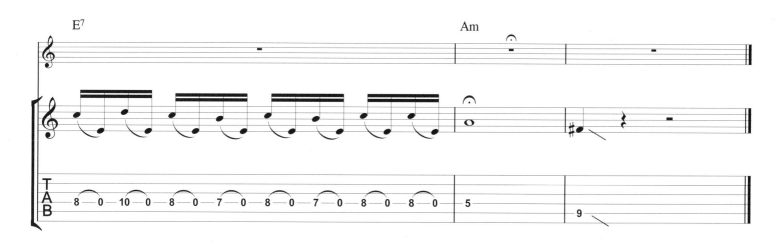

AGITATED

Lyrics & Music by Matthew Bellamy

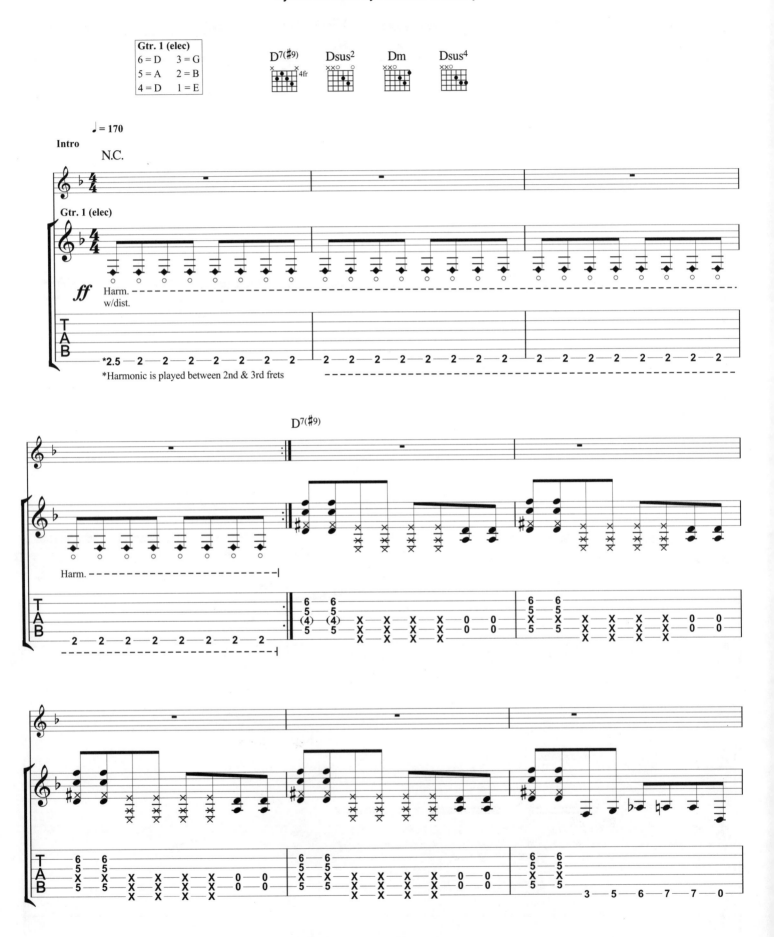

145

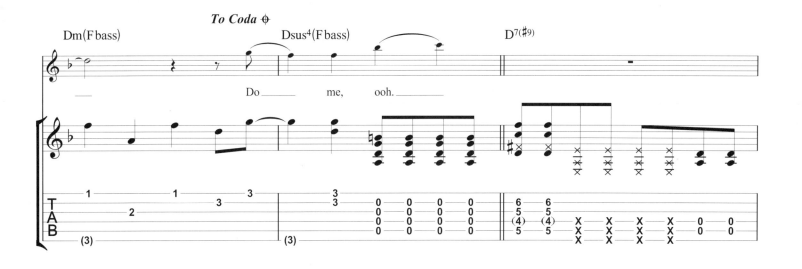

To Coda ⊕

Dm(F bass)   Dsus⁴(F bass)   D⁷⁽♯⁹⁾

Do ____ me, ooh.

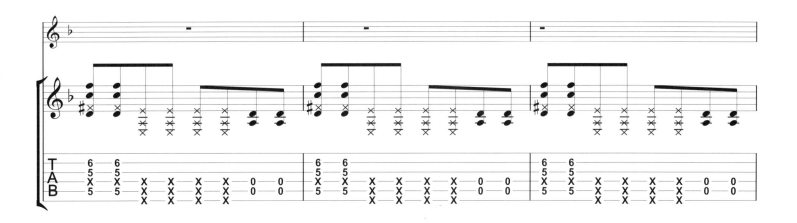

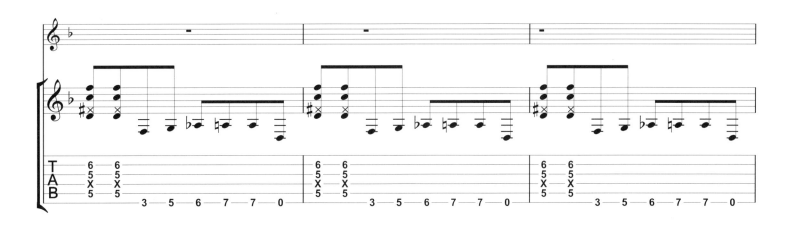

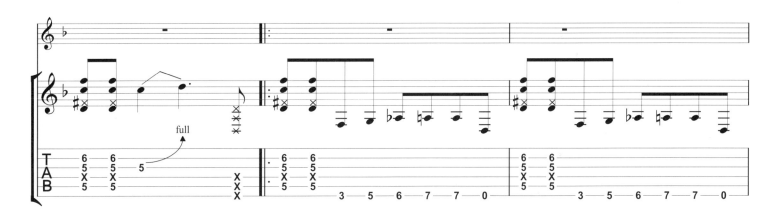

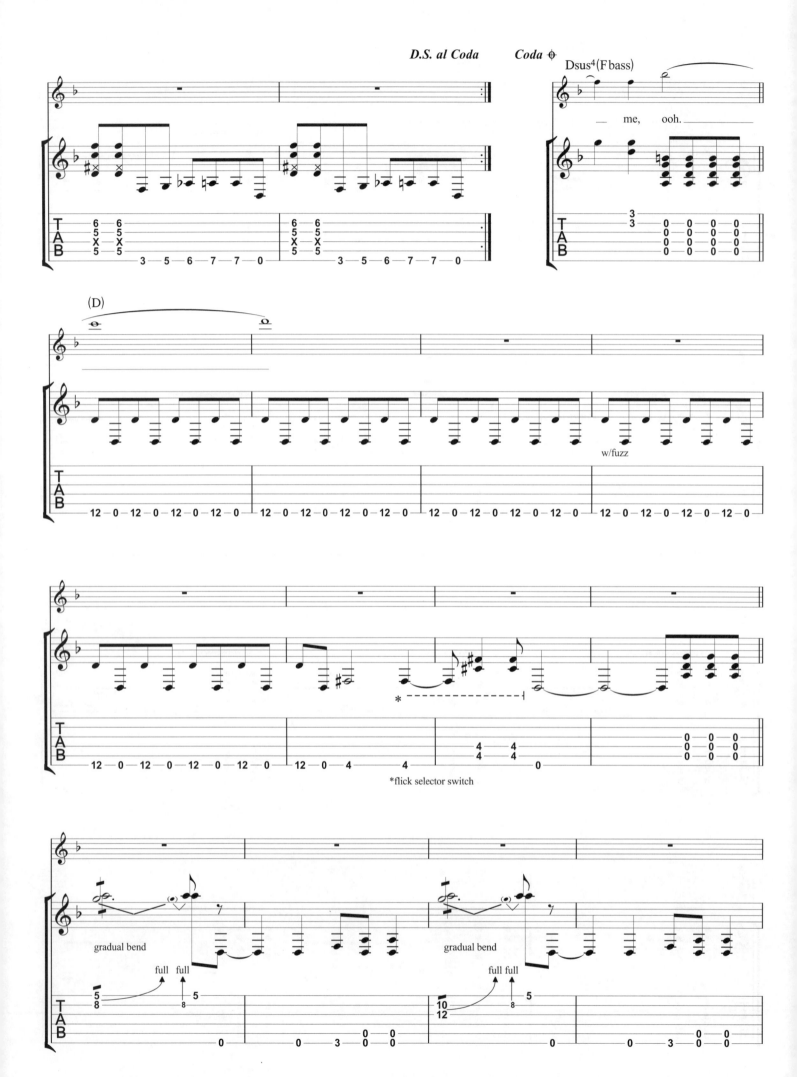

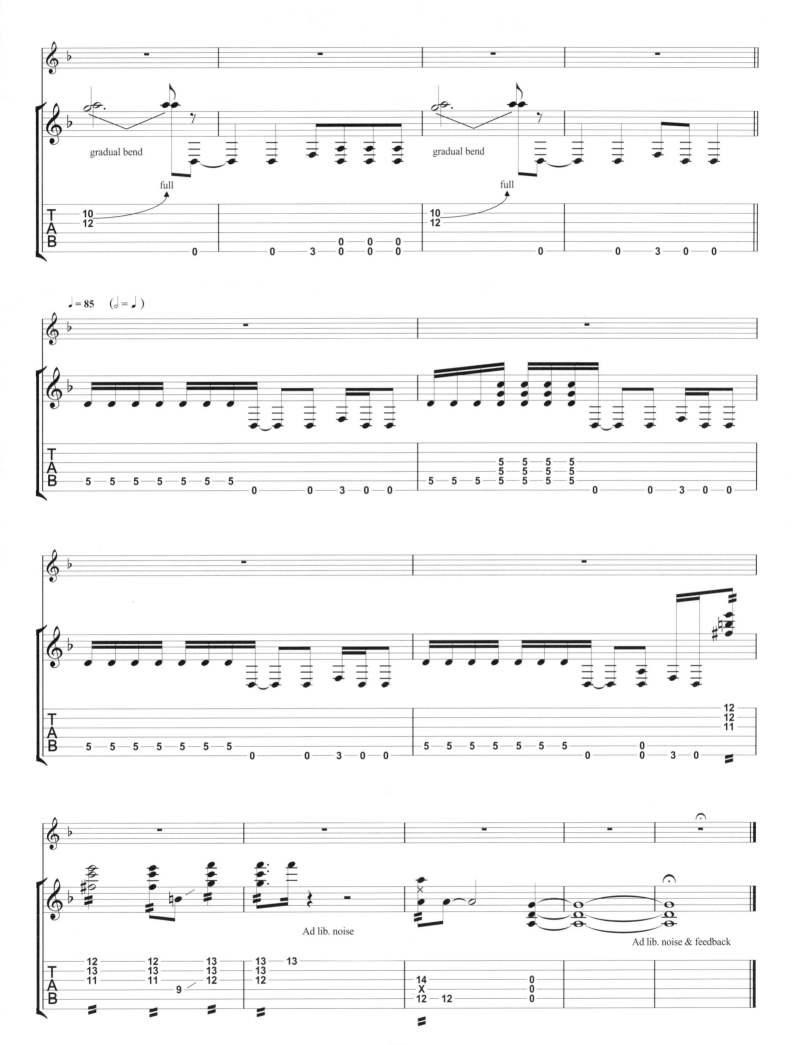

149

MUSCLE MUSEUM

Lyrics & Music by Matthew Bellamy

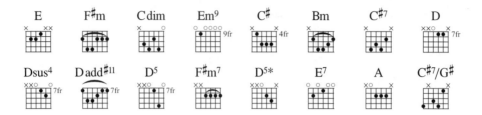

Intro
Free time

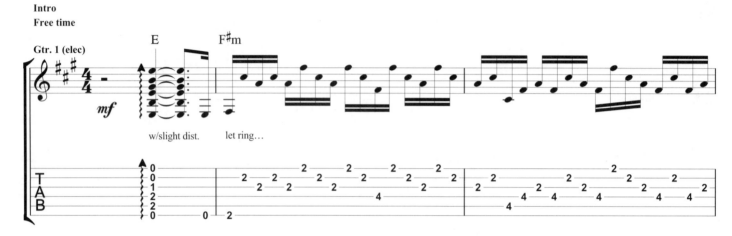

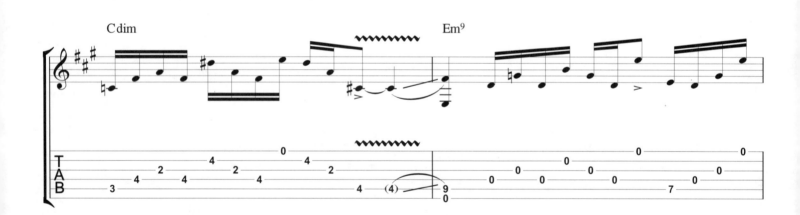

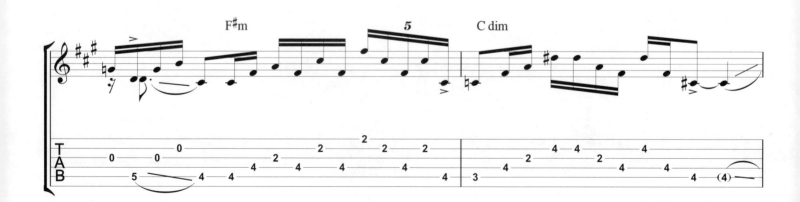

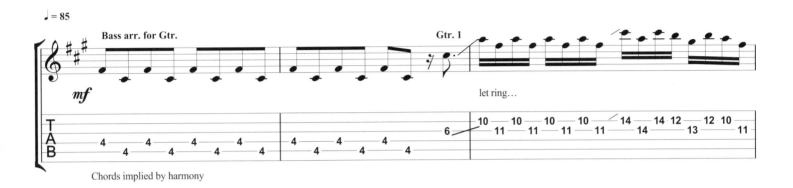

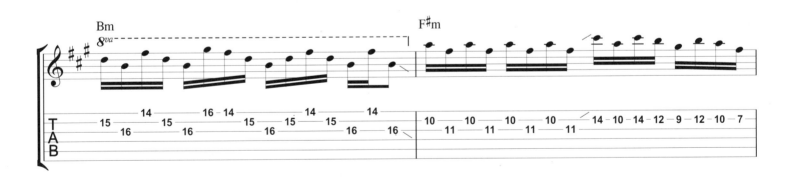

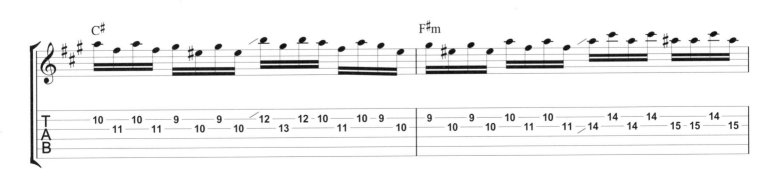

152

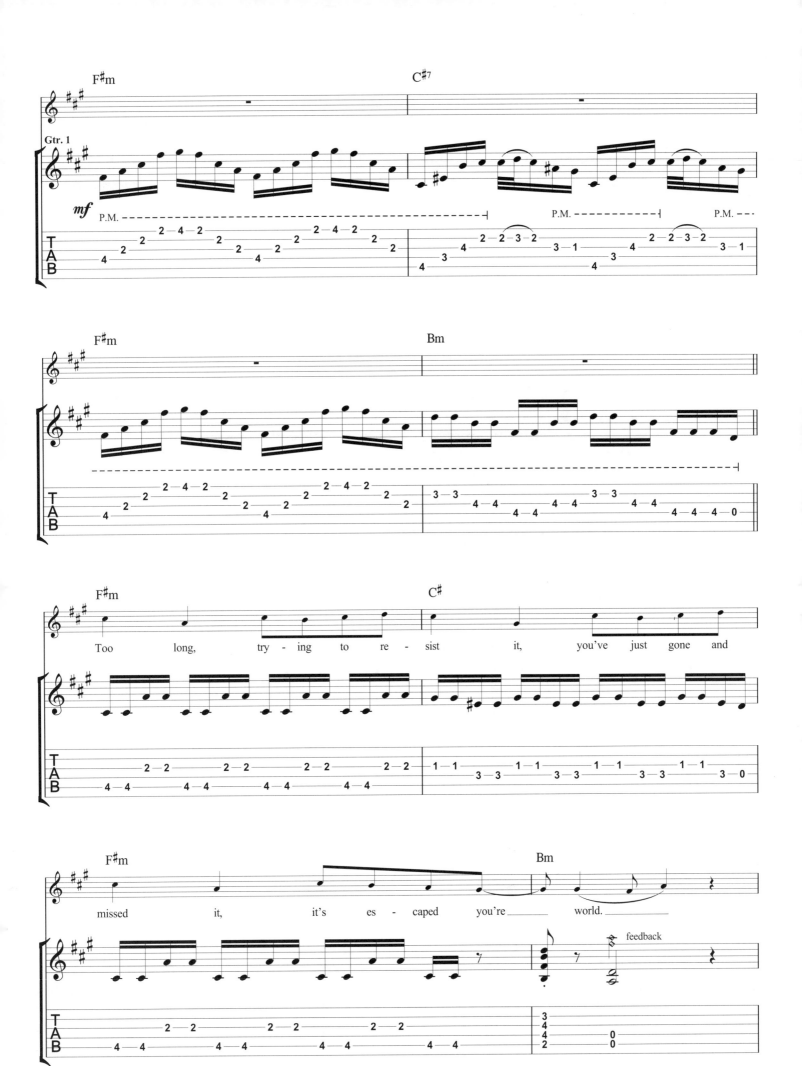

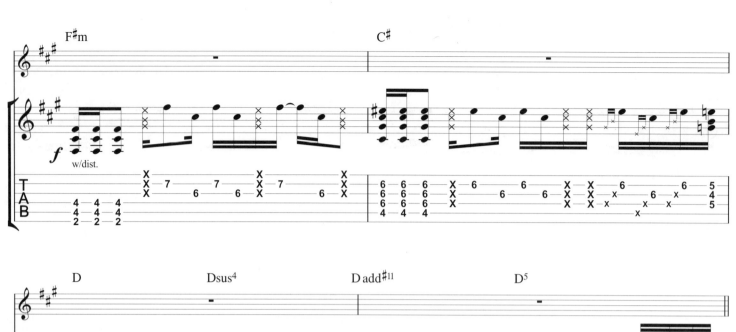

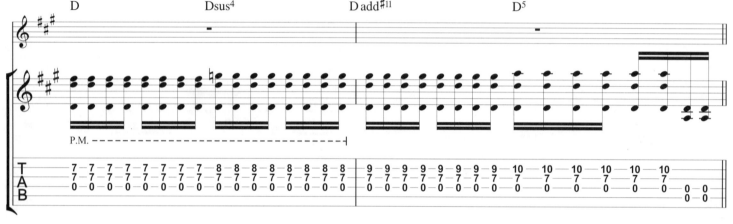

Chorus

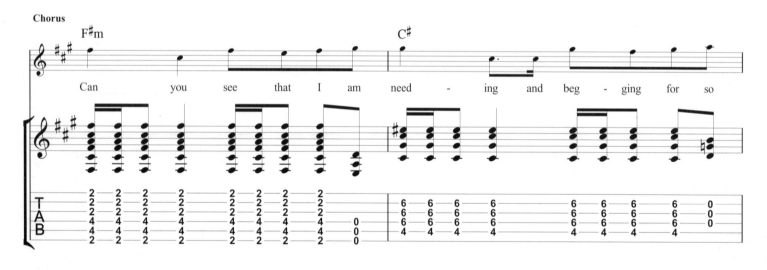

Can you see that I am need - ing and beg - ging for so

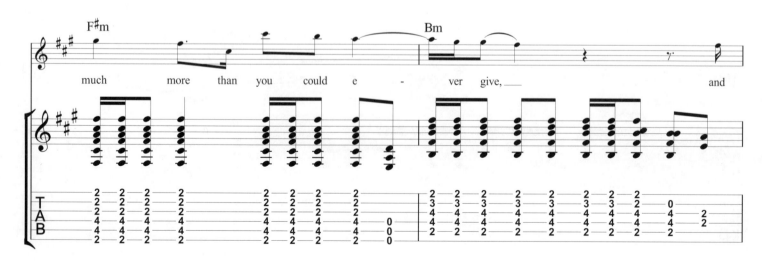

much more than you could e - ver give, ___ and

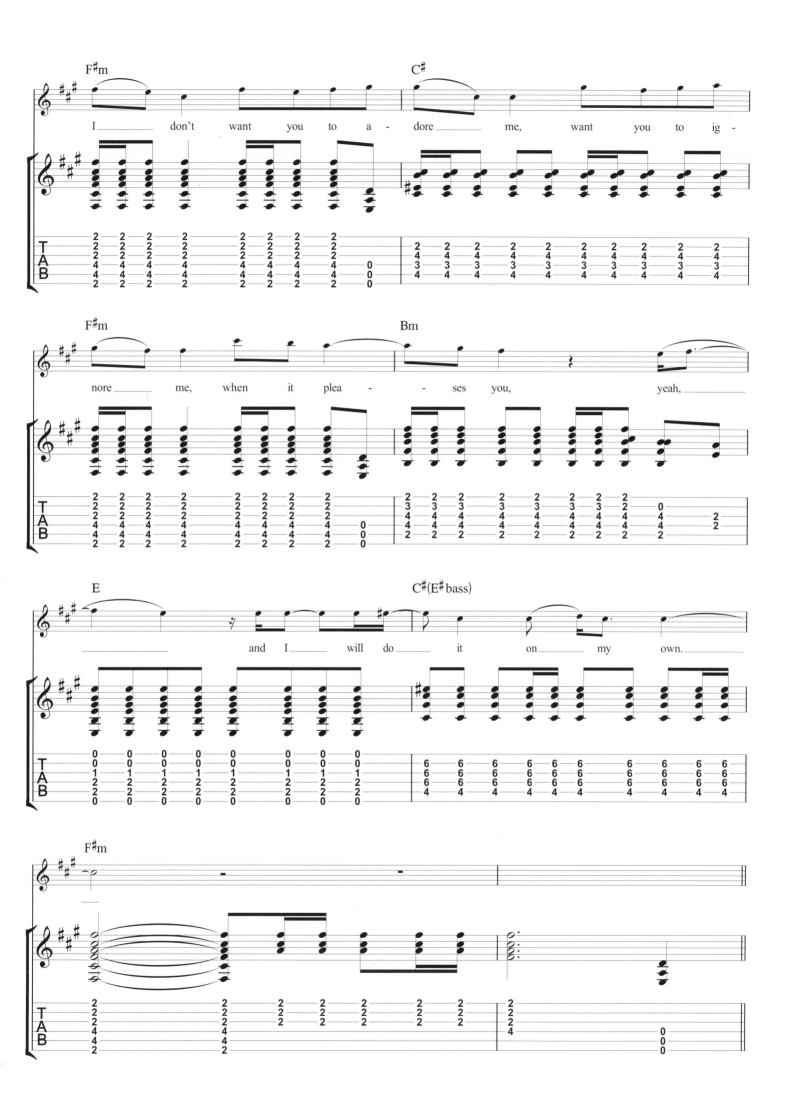

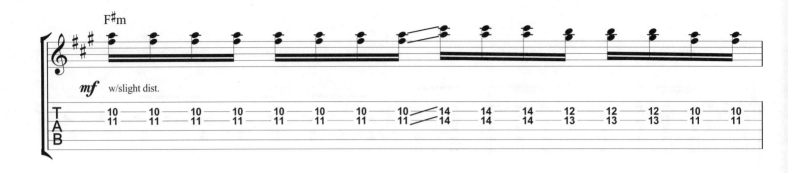

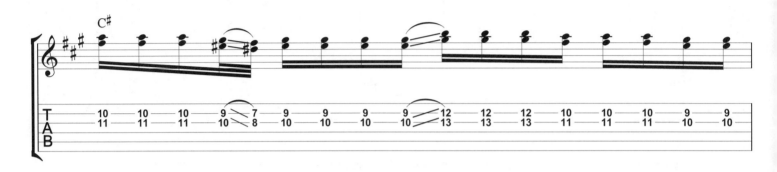

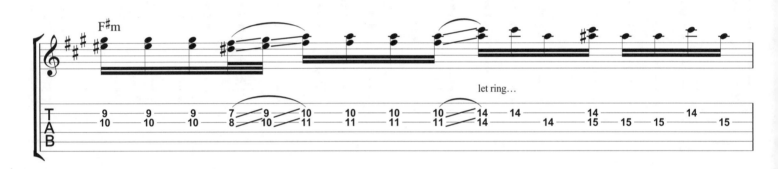

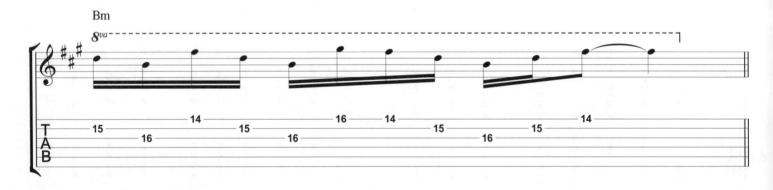

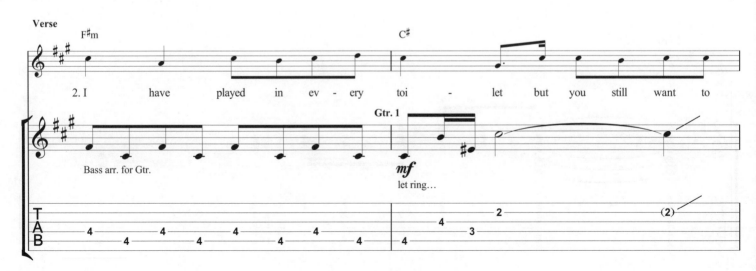

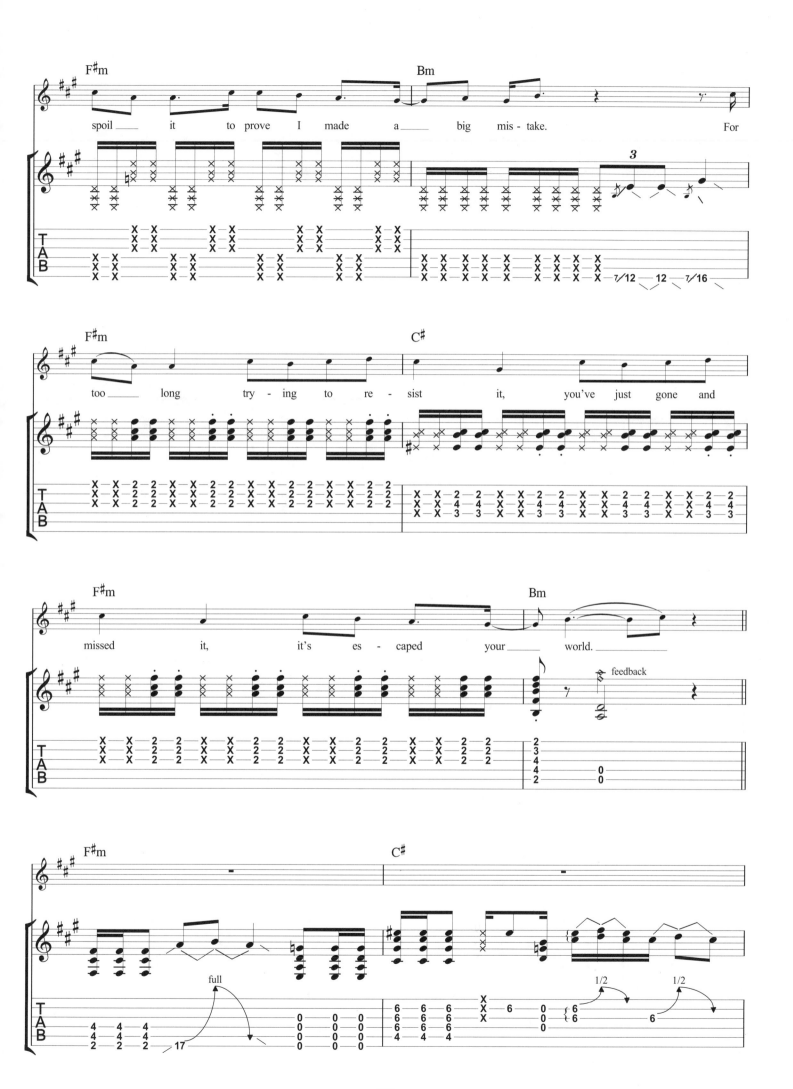

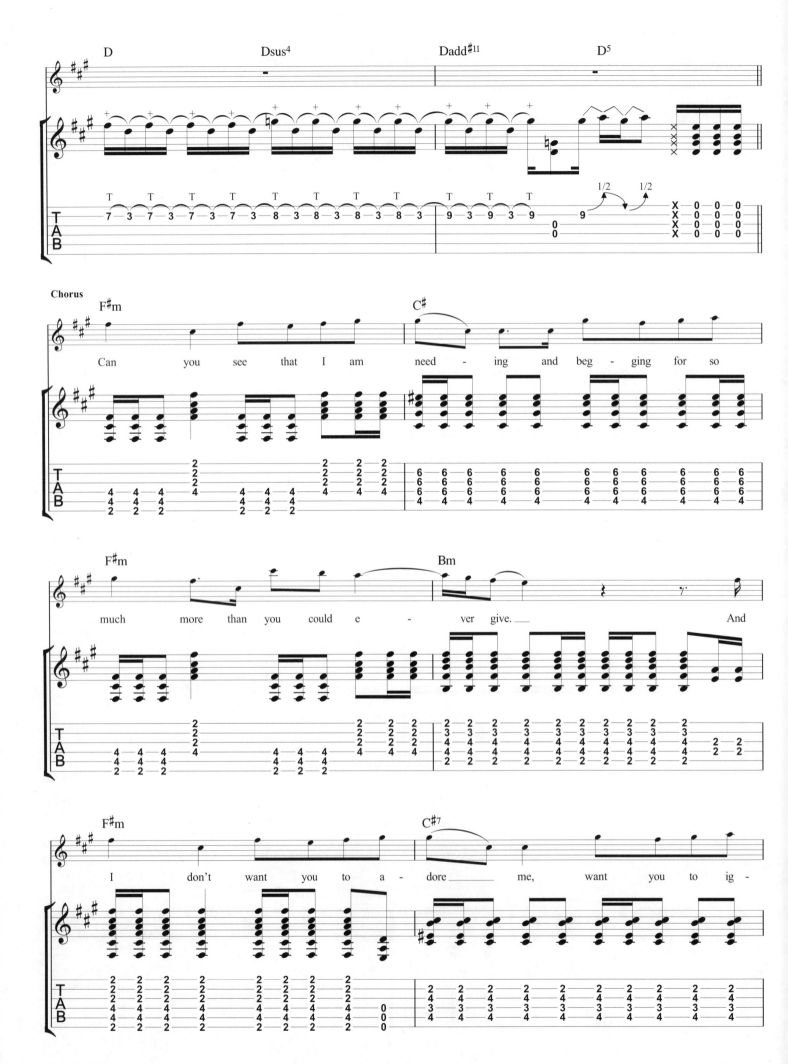

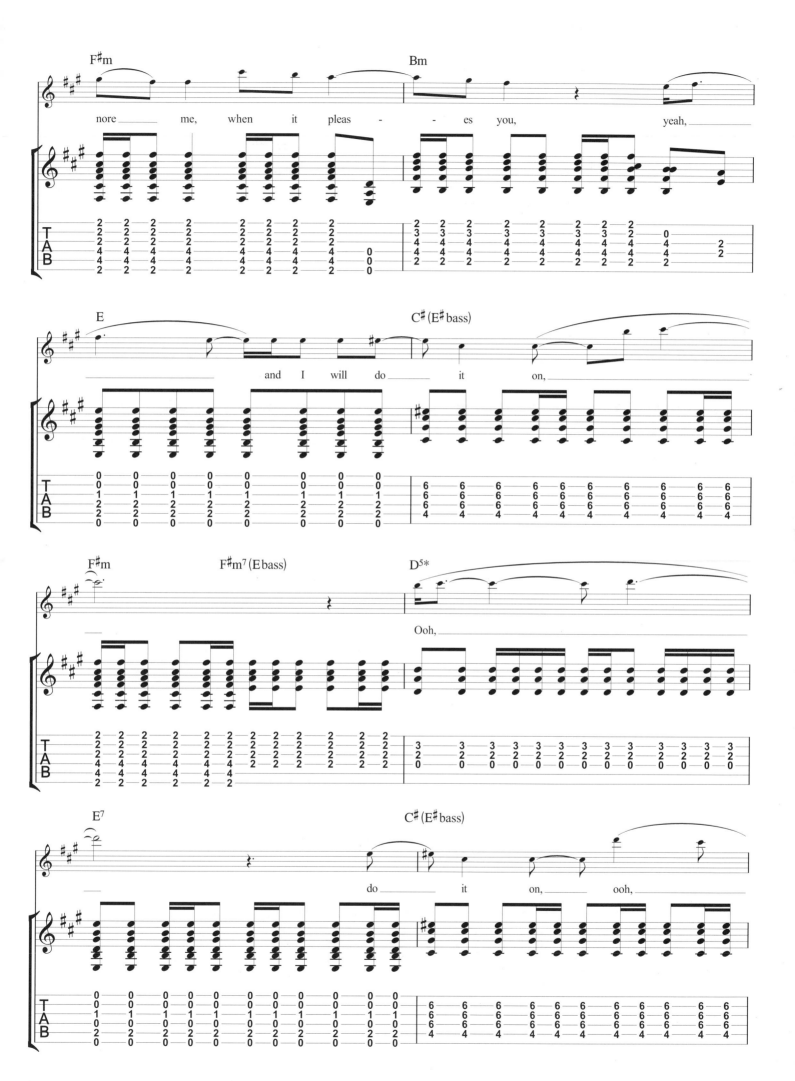

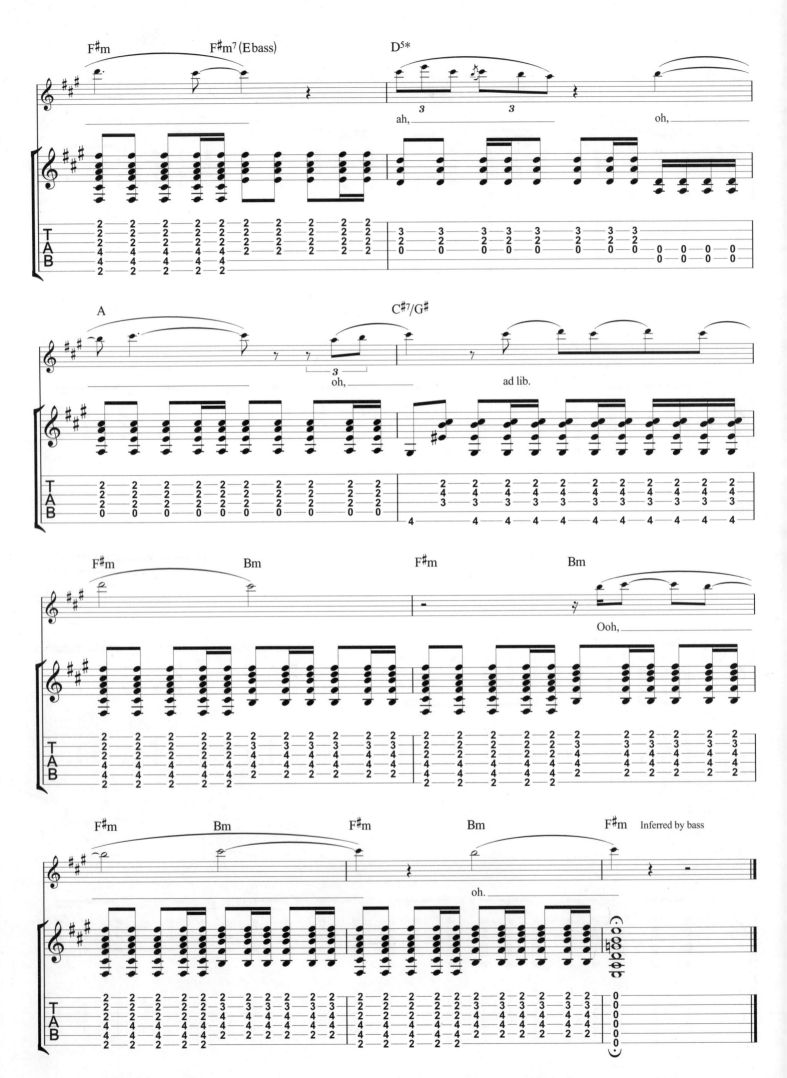